Illumination: Finding Light in Cancer's Shadow

(A Couple's Journey with Cancer)

By Linda Chung & Håkan BjÖrn

CONTENTS

FOREWORD

This book is about embracing the light while facing down a serious breast cancer diagnosis.

Initially written as a blog to keep our friends and family updated, Illumination will make you question your currently held beliefs about cancer, about suffering, about courage and what is truly important in life. With clear insight, compassion and tender-hearted confessions of love and grief, this book alternates between the perspective of Linda, the patient, and her husband, Håkan, and ultimately lifts you up with hope, comfort and a strong will to live a fulfilled life.

Join us on this extraordinary journey with cancer as we ultimately embrace acceptance and the light.

DEDICATION

To you, our dear friends, families, and clients who cheered us on, steadfastly and relentlessly, on this life-affirming and expanding experience. You brought light into our lives and infused the journey with so much grace. We are indeed not walking alone.

We are also extremely grateful to all the healthcare workers who dedicate their professional lives to helping other people. What a selfless endeavour!

In particular, the nurses and support staff at BC Cancer Centre have been instrumental in helping us keep our positive outlook. We also want to thank our amazingly skilled surgeons, radiologist and of course, our oncologist, Dr. Mitri, for his reassuring style, empathy and breadth of knowledge. You walked us through the toughest moments in our lives. Thank you.

Chapter 1
Bombshell

December 5, 2022

"THIS IS PRETTY SERIOUS"

Linda

A myriad of challenges show up in our lives. Each of these presents us with a choice: we can respond in a way that grows and expands us while lighting our path, or we can let these challenges drag us down into darkness. So, which do we choose? The light, of course. We choose illumination.

Plants naturally grow towards the sunlight that nourishes them. This instinct exists in humans too, though on an emotional level. We all feel it, but it's not an overwhelming compulsion. You have to choose to pursue illumination; it will not simply show up on its own. We strive towards the light, not only for ourselves but for the sake of those around us.

Today, the radiologist informs us that: "This is pretty serious." What he means is that the tumour he has just biopsied could well be the bad kind. This, of course, still has to be confirmed by the lab. I wonder what the point is of sharing the alarming news with me right then. Surely, there's no point in just frightening people? I want to be optimistic. Since I've always been healthy, I still think that this is probably just a matter of taking out the tumour and being done with it.

One step at a time is now our silent mantra: live in the now. Projecting all kinds of dark scenarios doesn't present any possible upside at the moment (does it ever?). So, we focus on living normally and just breathing. Still, the unsettling thought lingers and settles in the middle of my chest. "What if?"

WHERE THE WIND TAKES US

Håkan

From the outside, it may seem like the life Linda and I have shared has followed a somewhat haphazard path: meeting for the first time in South Korea, maintaining a long-distance relationship for a year while I was working in Seattle, moving first to Seoul so we could be together, then to my native Sweden, and finally settling in Canada. Yet, each step we took was deliberate. Though all the geographic, professional, and other changes we made as a couple may seem radical, there was a purpose and a plan behind each. Always with consensus, in sync and in command.

What, however, do you do when this control is snatched away from you; when you're confronted with a situation where you are no longer in charge? Well, there are only two options: deal with it, or let your mind, body, and soul get dragged along by circumstances.

We're not averse to the unknown. Our unconventional and idiosyncratic path in life has taught us that we can handle anything, including cancer and ultimately death. We'll deal with it and accept that the light is always there – as long as you seek it out.

December 22, 2022

THE PATHOLOGY REPORT

Linda

Our family doctor now has my pathology report – finally, a full week behind schedule. We're getting toward the end of the year and everyone is preparing for the holiday season. Hospitals and those who work in the healthcare system are no exception. Things are slowing down just when my life seems to have sped up.

An urgent phone meeting is called, just two days before our planned hiking trip to the Arizona desert. We are informed that the tumour is indeed cancerous and in fact aggressive, spreading outside its point of origin to lymph nodes quickly, requiring urgent medical intervention. We are advised to cancel any imminent travel plans. Appointments with the surgeon and the oncologist will be scheduled in the new year, after the holidays.

Now, dreadful reality sets in. I have cancer. And I cannot avoid chemo – five months of hell. Still, maybe, probably, hopefully, that's just an unpleasant step on the way to certain recovery. I'm used to being healthy and optimistic. For now, I just continue living the mantra: "One step at a time. Breathe".

December 24, 2022

UNRAVEL

Håkan

Have you ever seen somebody else's life flash before your eyes? And the irony of our intertwined lives is that mine, too, is rapidly unravelling in front of me. She is everything to me: my foundation, my rock, the solid ground I exist on and the air that I breathe. There is no Håkan without Linda. At least not this version of me that I've grown so fond of, so accustomed to, so comfortable with, the one I plan to live out my life being. What if?

I'm quietly panicking in slow motion.

December 25, 2022

NEWS TRAVELS FAST

Linda

When our friends and family hear about my cancer, they respond wildly differently. Some of them flat-out deny what's happening – it cannot be true, not for you, who has always been so healthy. Some of them are silent, not knowing how to broach the subject even though they'd probably like to show their support. Another approach is to simply reassure me that I'll be fine. This is a promise they cannot possibly make, though I appreciate the sentiment. There are always encouraging statistics to quote, so some resort to doing "research" in an attempt to console and comfort.

I, myself, run through possible reasons in my head, looking for some kind of logic to explain my situation.

When I was a girl, my periods started earlier than those of my peers – apparently a sign of high estrogen production, something that's associated with certain cancers. I also did a lot of drinking during my early adult years for social and work-related reasons. Several years ago, though, I quit alcohol altogether in favour of having a clearer head. But maybe this was too late? Alcohol has recently been found guilty of increasing the odds of breast and other cancers.

I never ate much meat in my life. My diet favours vegetables and seafood. We are more or less organictarian, favouring natural, chemical-free food. During the pandemic, however, I expanded into red meat territory quite a bit as I wanted to try various new recipes that II had never cooked before – Vietnamese meatball sandwiches, pork ribs, Thai beef salad. Was this a bad idea? Red meat, too, has been linked to cancer.

At one point in my life, I did have a stressful job. At the time, I didn't think I was under much strain – until my body started complaining because my mind wouldn't. Another possible contributor to health issues, maybe even if these show up years later.

So, is my cancer environmental or genetic? Who can say?

Of course, other than indulging our ever-pensive minds, the search for these kinds of answers has no real purpose. I know in my heart that it is *not* my fault.

I didn't choose cancer. It chose me instead.

December 28, 2022

DIAGNOSIS BUT NO PROGNOSIS

Linda

Since the pathologist's report arrived during the last workweek of the year, we have no doctor's appointments scheduled until January. Our first visit to the breast surgeon is on the 4th; we'll see the oncologist on the 6th. We have a diagnosis but no prognosis, yet. We know where we are but not what's going to happen. This information will be supplied by the oncologist.

With no firm expectation to latch onto, my monkey brain runs wild trying to fill in the gaps. I try to reason with my mind, telling it that assuming the worst – or anything for that matter – has no real benefit. We need to live today, in this moment, and not worry about what may be. Still, two weeks is a very long time when your life hangs in the balance. I become an expert at taming the monkey. Having some experience with meditation helps, but it's impossible to ignore the storm on my horizon.

Håkan and I walk, walk, and walk because it's such a soothing and reassuringly normal activity. We find comfort in movement.

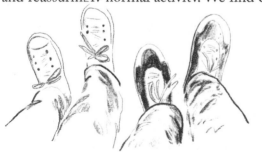

Hand in hand, yet we walk alone in our heads. Then, we're drawn back to one another. This alone time, combined with our togetherness, provides the peace and quiet we need to stay grounded in reality.

December 31, 2022

NEAR-DISASTERS

Håkan

You could say that cancer entering our lives is a catastrophe. It certainly has impact, a forceful, aggressive life of its own. But however anxious we feel right now, it doesn't mean we must expect and accept the worst.

I'm reminded of our last trip together before cancer. We spent a month in Croatia on the gorgeous Dalmatian coast. Our rental car made all kinds of anxiety-inducing beeps and alarming noises to alert us that we were getting too close to anything while parking or backing up. It also produced dings and whistles whenever we were speeding by a rosemary bush on the highway, or barely cleared a stone wall in a cramped village, or when a speeding truck decided to partially occupy our side of the road during a hairpin turn on the guardrail-less roads winding up the mountains.

Needless to say, you could not take your eyes off the road or hands off the steering wheel, not for a moment. Your sole occupation was to stay on the narrow ribbon of tarmac or gravel and survive. God save you if you needed to sneeze or otherwise lost focus for a nanosecond. You were on your own, buddy. Steep drop-offs into the blue, oh-so-blue Adriatic sea, that would gladly embrace you for eternity.

One morning, I was backing out from our very steep driveway on the impossibly beautiful Podgora coast when, suddenly, alarms went off and "bam!" the car slammed to a stop. I had no doubt that I had just run into the neighbour's craggy stone wall and completely ruined the back bumper. Our vacation was ruined; we were now facing serious insurance rigmarole in a country where we didn't know the system or speak the language.

Well, as it turns out, the car was way smarter than me and had automatically braked before we hit anything and saved the day! Not a scratch. No deductible or interminable phone calls. No squabbling with the credit card company to try to figure out how to pay for this disaster…that never happened, though I was certain it had.

How many disasters in our lives never actually happen, regardless of our fears? Tons, I'm sure. We just don't realize how often everything turns out just fine, exactly the way it was supposed to. Even when we think things are going wrong and the whole world is against us, is it really? Maybe these moments are lessons, teaching us to not be so sure all the time, to be more humble and grateful for what is and what we have.

Even if I had crashed the car into that stone wall, no one would have been hurt. Not the end of the world. Cars can be fixed. Money is just an arbitrary instrument which also can be replaced. Near-disasters; always there, waiting to happen. Really, though, there's just as much happiness and gratitude lurking about, around every corner. All we need to do is to recognize how fortunate we are. All the time, even when we're faced with potentially devastating news.

EVERYTHING IS SHATTERED

Our world has shattered
But everything still matters
Unfriend the pain and empty the tears

Everything is shattered
Yet everything still matters
Unfriend our grief and send off the fear

Everything's in tatters
And we are all that matters
Hold on to the light until the dark clouds clear

To listen to the song that resulted from this poem, check out:
https://hawkbjorn.com/there-are-days-like-these/

Chapter 2
At War with Cancer

January 4, 2023

THE BREAST SURGEON

Linda

For the foreseeable future, we're going to be spending time in doctors' offices like other people visit hair salons and cafes. The long-awaited start to these medical appointments is today, when we meet the breast surgeon for the first time.

A nurse comes out first, a very warm smile on her face, and she introduces herself. To my surprise, she hugs me and puts a very gentle hand on my shoulder, with no words spoken but saying: "I'm sorry about what you're going through." She oozes compassion. I'm surprised at the impact that the little gesture has on me. My heart warms instantly.

She leads us into a room with a tiny bed which even I, a small person, cannot fit onto. Then we're left cooling our heels for a very long time before the surgeon turns up. I note her age and interpret it as experience. Then, I wonder as well if doctors can get jaded after so many years of saving lives (and occasionally failing to).

She is "surgical" in her manner, no pun intended. I'm not kidding. She speaks to the point, wasting no words. She immediately asks what I know so far. She is exactly the opposite of her nurse. Bless her heart, she is likely very good at her job but could probably apply a little more empathy to the way she expresses herself. She bluntly tells us that the surgery will happen after chemotherapy and implies that this specific type of cancer is trickier than most. It's the oncologist who can explain the prognosis with authority, however. In either case, it seems that my battle with cancer is not going to be a brief brawl, but instead a long fight.

The doctor delivers all of this without a word of reassurance. With this news, we are finally confronting the worst-case scenario. My mind races, thinking about wrapping up my life. As long as we're not forced to consider it, we all assume that our health is fine. This false sense of security, which I enjoyed even though I knew what the prognosis might be, has now been taken away from me.

In some ways, I probably preferred my former uncertainty to knowing the truth. Which is more frightening: the question you cannot answer, or the answer you cannot accept?

January 5, 2023

THE TRUTH IS SOMETIMES HARD TO HEAR

Håkan

The truth is sometimes hard to hear
And harder still to accept
So much of our reaction is fear
Of a future unmet

Yes, the truth is sometimes hard to hear
But truth is like a compass on the open seas
We need it to find our way home from there
Back to the heart of our peace

January 6, 2023

GOOD NEWS, BAD NEWS

Linda

Today, we see my oncologist for the first time. During this marathon meeting, lasting two hours and then some, he and his team lay out their plan to eliminate what appears to be stage-2, aggressive, HER2-positive cancer. HER2 is a kind of fast-growing breast cancer – bad news. On the other hand, the very fact that it is so aggressive makes it an easier target for chemo. The sort-of-good news is therefore that it responds well to treatment. I can also be thankful for the fact that we caught it in time. If I had allowed fear or denial to rule my actions and delayed getting the mammogram, my options would have been far worse and fewer.

So I have a new label for me and others to apply to myself: I have HER2-positive, hormone-negative breast cancer. There's nothing about this we're allowed to take with a grain of salt.

The idea of "good news" becomes very relative when you have cancer. What I have to look forward to is five months of chemotherapy (two general chemo agents and two drugs that specifically target HER2), followed by surgery, radiation, and more drug therapies. All together, and if it goes well, my treatment will last about a year. If it doesn't go well? The oncologist has a phrase he tends to say often: "We will cross that bridge when we get there." Wise words, indeed. Presumably, he has a contingency plan, one which involves not letting me worry unnecessarily ahead of time.

Our oncologist (who is great by the way, not only skilled in his field but a kind, clear and empathetic communicator) also informs us that the prognosis is "in our favour". This means a great deal to us; the first glimmer of light in a whole month of progressively worse news.

The oncologist draws a neat diagram to show us what my treatment will look like over the next six months and which chemos and chemo-prepping medicine I'll need to take. This visual representation helps us understand the journey. Better the devil you know! It's amazing how setting out everything on one piece of paper makes the road ahead seem less intimidating and hopeless. Seeing how all the steps fit together crystalizes all this new, unfamiliar, and scary information for us. The diagram also demonstrates that, though I have a lot still to go through, completing each stage will mean taking a giant step in the right direction. I no longer have to think of the various treatments in my future as things that will be done to me; rather, I can see each as a blow I will strike against my cancer.

He also confirmed what we already knew: that I should expect severe side effects. These will include hair loss: I will be completely bald within three to six weeks at the latest. I don't think that I'm particularly vain, but this change in appearance will make it hard to ignore the fact that I'm soon not going to be as vital and capable as I'm used to being. He gives us a whole sheaf of prescriptions to treat the expected side effects, including a prescription for a wig, in a thick envelope, along with more information than we can really absorb at this point.

The first chemo is scheduled for two weeks from now.

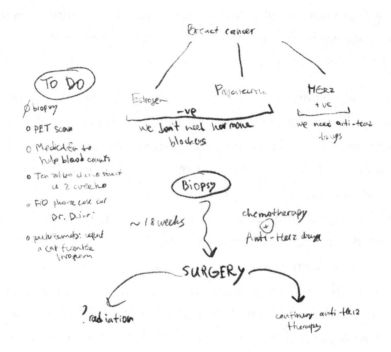

A NEW WAY OF LIVING

Linda

My relationship with pain often surprises the people who know me. They expect that I should handle pain better than the average person because I can deal with things like stress and life challenges relatively easily. On the contrary, I'm terrible with pain and suffering. I don't like needles and I definitely prefer comfort to foregoing medication. This isn't so strange: I used to be a very healthy person and pain hasn't been a big part of my life – aside from emotional hurts, of which I have had plenty.

So, anticipating a deluge of pain and discomfort, Håkan and I go into overdrive – buying up all kinds of medication in preparation for any and all possible side effects. It's inevitable that these will start appearing soon, but which ones I'll suffer and how severe they'll be is anyone's guess. Cancer has a habit of surprising you – whatever you may have been expecting.

Our oncologist shares with us that the way we treat cancer hasn't changed all that much over the past few decades. How we manage the side effects of the toxic "medicine", however, has. So, I'm arming myself with a multicoloured rainbow of pills that takes up a whole new shelf in the kitchen. What used to be my creative space (culinary and otherwise) has now turned into our medical command centre. For that matter, I don't think I'll be cooking much for a while anyways.

January 7, 2023

I WILL RALLY BUT NOT TODAY

Håkan

Just let me be
So I can breathe and pray
I will rally
But not today

Give me time
To throw my fears away
I will rally
But not today

Give me peace
And give me strength
I must rally
But not today

Let me hold you tightly
Let me hear you say
"I will rally
And live another day"

January 14, 2023

LEFT BEHIND

Linda

Strangely (and perhaps not so surprisingly), I feel at ease thinking about the possibility of my life ending. Impermanence is the essence of nature – everything is born, grows, changes and dies. Death has simply moved from an abstract notion to a firm reality for me today.

Naturally, I reflect on the past and ask THE question: "Do I have any regrets? Will I spend the rest of my time differently with this finality in mind?" Thinking about the life I've led, I discover that I'm not haunted by disappointment – I lived my recent years by design, not by default. I chose my own values instead of accepting those others tried to foist off on me and, by and large, lived accordingly. Of course, there's always room for improvement: compliments given instead of reserved, adventures embraced rather than avoided, knowledge gained instead of rejected. Maybe I can be more generous and kinder to others from here on out. I will be!

I can go now, if it comes to that. But what about Håkan? The prospect of leaving him behind causes me great sadness. A cold, hard sorrow has been lying coiled in my chest ever since the biopsy. It seems like it has made this spot its permanent home. It's always waiting, dormant; any little thing can trigger it and bring tears to my eyes: an ever-so-slight change in the wind, the blue sky we used to go hiking under, sympathetic words from a friend, his favourite food...well, anything, you name it.

We each seem to be trying to hide our own moments of private sorrow from the other. Sure, after I'm gone, he will have other, new, exciting opportunities and experiences. Yet, the thought of him grieving alone, for however long it might be, is unbearable.

We have a friend who is 86 years old, who lost her spouse to cancer a few years ago. She lacks nothing in her life, yet everything! Her late husband was her light. I see glimpses of shadows in her eyes when she talks about him, which is often. In most ways, she is such a positive and bubbly person. Yet the ache is there, plain as day.

I think about Håkan being alone. He wrote a pretty sad song called "Life Insurance" more than a decade ago after we had a meeting with a prospective financial advisor who was adamant about selling us life insurance. When we didn't bite, he became outright rude.

"If it happens and you leave before I do", Håkan sings, "I won't need any life insurance. A simple boat will do". The idea is that he'll row miles into the ocean and drop the oars. And then: "I will lie down and close my eyes. And I'll wait – until I drift back to you". I know he's a romantic and this is an ultimate statement of love. I also know he's a sensible guy, so he won't act on the song. But I get it, how he feels.

And so I share my empathy with the world, for whoever has lost their life companions.

January 16, 2023

LIKE SQUIRRELS BEFORE WINTER

Linda

We're also stocking up on foods that are high in nutrition, easy to digest, and good for nausea – broth, herbal teas, yogurt, sports drinks, and so on. Some other sopping we're doing really brings home what I'm about to go through, like picking up all the drugs that are supposed to help ease the chemo's side effects…along with a bucket to keep next to my bed.

Along the way, Håkan is busy navigating the healthcare labyrinth. Canada's public healthcare system is way more efficient and comprehensive than some of its detractors make it out to be – becoming very sick in a country where we'd also have to deal with an insurance company or clumsy bureaucracy would have been really bad luck. Still, it certainly doesn't cover everything. We'll have to pay out of our own pocket for a couple of expensive drugs that have yet to be approved by the British Columbia government but have nevertheless been recommended by my doctors. What Håkan's discovered isn't always great news, but we focus on the positive – what IS covered and available.

I wonder how others travel this journey with financial challenges. My heart goes out to them. We (or rather, most of us) like to assume that every human life is inherently priceless: young and old, man or woman, rich and poor. Finance and economics, however, have no time for this kind of sentiment.

GINGER ALE

Håkan

Like professional athletes getting ready for a big championship match, we prepare carefully, discuss strategies, take stock of what we already have and what we need, anticipate and talk through the possible scenarios. If this happens, then what? Tactics. Except this is no sports event and we are certainly not experienced professionals. More like frenzied amateurs trying to learn the rules of the game just as the referee blows the starting whistle.

Still, we prepare as best as we can. Over-prepare, probably. When so much is beyond our control and even understanding, making plans and taking concrete steps for the things we can manage provides a much-needed sense of accomplishment and stability. We've received plenty of good (and sometimes less good) advice, but it's clear that there is only so much we can do in a practical sense. The rest is up to fate (or a deity, if you prefer) but hopeful actions at least help to keep us on an even keel.

Ginger tea and ginger ale are often recommended for reducing nausea while at the same time providing hydration. So, I steep fresh ginger to make huge batches of ginger tea. And I must have gone to five different stores trying to find the most natural brand of ginger ale. Most of them are packed full of sugar and artificial ingredients – not our usual diet at all, and right now is probably not the time to start making needless changes. I finally find one that contains actual ginger instead of flavouring! I buy a whole bunch, enough to hydrate an entire football team.

January 17, 2023

RULES TO LIVE BY

Linda

As part of this whole experience – even though the real ordeal hasn't started yet – I've also decided that I'll need to swap out some of my core values. As a business coach, I've found that defining these makes them much easier to live by. It may seem strange, but our internal compasses don't always or automatically point to true north. Understanding which values are most important helps us stay on track, especially when we're stressed and afraid.

In my case, efficiency and self-reliance (or freedom, in my vocabulary) used to be the most important principles I strived to embody. At least temporarily, I'm going to replace these with acceptance, gratitude, and courage.

Acceptance

I could start by asking: "Why me?" but I choose to phrase this as: "Why *not* me?" If one in eight women has to contract breast cancer, I actually prefer it to be me. I am relatively young and healthy. Having practised meditation for over four years now, I have a better relationship with my mind than ever. I'm also fortunate to live in a gorgeous place with a sound healthcare system. I know, intellectually, that "falling on my sword" doesn't mean somebody else won't get cancer, but counting my blessings and tallying up my advantages makes accepting this misfortune that much easier.

I will need to accept things as they are, instead of complaining about how they should or could be. If I need to slow down, I shall. I will rely on others. I'll say "yes" to help, a lot, acknowledging the current reality instead of automatically searching for ways things can be improved. I have a feeling that I will grow the most in this area.

I don't know how my body will respond to the treatments or what kind of side effects will torment me. I will have to accept them as they come, however bad they may be. One step at a time! I'm used to doing several things at once, so there's another thing to accept.

Gratitude

It's always a good idea to be grateful and positive whenever possible... and it's always possible! People think that gratitude is something you practice for others; in fact, it's something you do for yourself. The mental benefits are immediate and enormous.

We're both grateful that we have each other. I know that I have the best possible partner to share this journey with. We are grateful to live in a comfortable home and aware of how nearby nature embraces and soothes us.

In general, hopefully, we'll still have our health (yes, I know it sounds a bit like a contradiction). A friend told us that cancer doesn't discriminate between healthy and unhealthy lifestyles or physiques. Even if this is true, though, a person who is in good shape is naturally better able to handle the bodily assaults to come.

We've also experienced some amazing, heartfelt friendship and support so far. Who would have thought being diagnosed with cancer could be such an enriching experience, even if only in this sense? Does this kind of challenge bring loved ones closer? I bet it does.

Courage

In the very near future, I'll need to be brave enough to let go of my long-established self-image: a healthy person, with vitality, plenty of energy and, yes, abundant hair. I hate pain, yet I'll have to learn to embrace or at least tolerate it. The suffering to come causes me great anxiety, and this is just one of the symptoms and side effects I'll have to make friends with even while every part of my body is protesting. Now, just a couple of hours remain before my chemo appointment. I wonder how I will find myself on the other side. We will see......

January 17, 2023

DIS-APPEARING

Håkan

You're disappearing. And so am I. We're both disappearing I guess.
And still, we're connected. The past carries us into the now.
And possibly the future. Everything is always possible, isn't it?
One day you appeared. So did I. We both appeared I guess.
At the same time. Connected. To our past and present.
And what a wide-eyed future to have!
The wind rushes through my hair
We glance into each other's eyes
Smiles flicker across our faces
You. I. We. Together. Always!

To listen to the song that resulted from this poem, check out:
https://hawkbjorn.com/i-will-rally-but-not-today/

Chapter 3
Two In a Boat

January 18, 2023

THE FIRST CHEMO

Linda

I recall a national exam that I took many years ago. In Korea, high school students in their final year, most of whom aspire to go to "good" universities and subsequently lead prosperous lives, are all graded on this test and were, back then, placed into different categories based on the results. Everyone was just as nervous as I was.

This one single exam determines your entire life's course and the level of success you can expect to achieve – well, almost. Needless to say, it's a stressful event as well as a kind of rite of passage. I don't know why I am reminded of this on our way to the British Columbia Cancer Centre for my first infusion of chemo. The feeling of wishing that I was done with it already, maybe. In fact, I wish that I were done with the whole chemo program. Even better, done with the entire upcoming year. I know... I am way ahead of myself here. I know I'm in for a marathon; trying to sprint through it won't help.

I'm aware of the Centre's reputation as one of the best in the world. I'd heard of their holistic support and excellent standard of care even before I knew anything about cancer. One of the things that delights Håkan, perhaps disproportionately, is free parking. Guess what! BC Cancer patients are provided with a one-year parking pass at their facilities to cover the full treatment program. This is just one way to reduce the stress cancer patients and their families are already under. A small but good example to illustrate how the Centre's support goes above and beyond simply treating disease.

Their reputation may have reduced my anxiety a bit. Ever so calm, organized and confident, the chemo nurses are each focused on their own tasks when we arrive. This display of professionalism also takes some of the edge off. Our nurse, originally from Scotland, leads us into a room where there are already two other patients hooked up to IVs. One much older lady and another youngish, wearing a beanie, say hello to me. Both share a gentle smile as if to say: "You will be alright."

We patients are provided with airplane-style reclining armchairs like those you find in first class, while our families or friends sit on small, hard chairs, as if in economy – well, maybe not even that. We joke about it briefly before the nurse prepares a warm towel to prime my veins. So, it begins! The first of many to come.

I squeeze Håkan's hand when the IV is inserted and twisted in. The nurse checks if we brought our nausea medicine, which I will need to take half an hour before one of the chemo agents. Of course, we did. I'm generally pretty organized but I now leave all of this to Håkan, as he takes his job of preparation and support very seriously.

Then there are these frozen gloves, which may help prevent Docetaxel (one of the chemo drugs) from inducing nail toxicity. If this should occur, the most likely result is just that my fingernails won't be especially attractive to look at. However, more severe effects are possible, some of which could effectively mean losing the use of my fingers for several weeks.

Getting my hands frozen is highly, highly unpleasant to someone like me who really dislikes cold things. I endure it for about two hours, with lots of warm blankets supplied by the nurse and Håkan, who quickly learns where the warming cupboard is located and bustles about the place like an extra-tall, substitute nurse getting water, hot tea, blankets, warm towels and anything else I ask for. It really *is* like flying first class, except for the IV in my hand and, well, pretty much everything else.

These first few sessions are extra long, since they need to watch my body's response to the toxins that are being introduced. Observation periods of 30 minutes to one hour are necessary after every chemo infusion. Everyone is on alert for sudden allergic reactions. I see that the nurse wears an additional gown whenever she handles the chemo drugs. It's not hard to notice how toxic these drugs really are. War is never pretty!

I outfitted myself for almost a full day of treatment by lining up a podcast playlist. Half distracted, I listen to the Economist world events. The war in Ukraine is still wreaking havoc in my ears while I fight another war inside.

Many hours seem to have passed when the nurse finally says that I'm done for the day. Leaving the ward after a long day at the British Columbia Cancer Centre, we can't help but feel relieved to have my first chemo session behind us. Other than having to take a sleeping pill in the middle of the night to combat the steroids' effects, I feel relatively unscathed. Yes, side effects are only supposed to start in earnest in a little while. But what's the point of anticipating the worst, really? Again, it's best to live in (and appreciate) the moment.

There's currently an unbelievable amount of medication running through my system. The idea, obviously, is to overwhelm and kill the cancer cells, including any that may have split off from the tumours in my left breast to hide in other parts of my body and create new cancer nodes. The drugs are designed to target these, but this is far from perfect: all this poison kills many healthy cells as well. So, to combat that, I've already injected, swallowed, and otherwise applied all sorts of other "helpful" drugs. Some of these have their own side effects I'll need to contend with, but luckily none of them are nearly as aggressive as the chemo.

Things are going to get much worse before they get better. I have some extremely unpleasant days ahead of me. Still, obsessing over a murky future can only bring a shadow into my soul. Instead, I plan to focus on those feelings that illuminate the here and now: joy, love, hope.

January 19, 2023

TWO IN A BOAT

Linda

A friend sent me this beautiful poem, so apt for going through this journey of cancer treatment together, Håkan and I. How can I ever thank you enough, my sweetest, most devoted, quiet warrior? In you, you carry such wisdom, patience, and ever-growing (if this were even possible, yet it still is) love and care. I will fight this fight thanks to you, because of you first and foremost, before I think of the rest of us. Thanks, dear Meg, for sending this poem to us. You know us so well!

Two in a Boat

There are
two of them
In a boat,
One reads
the stars,
The other
finds the way through the storms,
When one
navigates the stars,
The other
leads through the storms,
And then,
at the end, at the very end,
They'll
remember

The sea was
blue.

– Reiner Kunze (Translation by Victoria Ichizli-Bartels)

January 20, 2023

LABRADOR

Håkan

Life turns into a kind of quiet, singular-focus, slow-motion routine. All I think about is how to keep her as comfortable as possible, preparing our home with comfy blankets, soft pillows out on the sofa, and new bed linen. I've also stocked up on all kinds of nourishing liquids – coconut water, organic apple juice, watermelon juice, and natural ginger ale for nausea. I don't know how much, or if at all, these will help to ease Linda's discomfort. At least I'll be able to keep her hydrated, which is apparently very important when going through chemo.

I become a hyper-active labrador. Any hint, whimper, look of discomfort, gesture of pain, and I spring into action and ask the ever-recurring question: "What can I do to make it better?" The hard part is: sometimes there's nothing you can do. Restoring sleep to a sleepless, nauseous, suffering body is not in your power. Curing painful mouth sores, not in your wheelhouse. So, you suffer along, feeling a now-familiar helplessness, a loss of control. Except you don't have to. Instead, I hold her hand. Bring a cool washcloth. Offer a soothing mouth drop. Smile at her. Hold her. Just hold her. For as long as it takes.

January 22, 2023

TIME

Linda

After two drug-heavy days, during which I felt like my body was made of lead, I am up like clockwork at 2:25 a.m. the last few nights. I could choose to be resentful and frustrated. I decide to embrace it instead. I'm warm in our comfortable bed and not feeling too queasy. I'm grateful for that. I will make friends with you, the waking one, and not resent you.

Time is a funny thing. Our perception of it matters so much and often has little to do with a clock or a calendar. Time in our head can be ever-abundant or eternally scarce. I note that cancer does one thing very well – it focuses you on what truly matters. Perhaps as a result, I find that the amount of time I have available is just perfect: not too much, not too little. Maybe it's always like that when you neither hurry nor procrastinate.

I was certainly given many blessings, along with some significant deficiencies including arrogance. When I made the decisions that I did, I knew and trusted only so much. Even today, I can only think and decide according to my own capacities and the information available to me. All in all, the life that I lived wasn't a perfect one, but then again, does anyone lead a perfect life? We do our best.

I am okay with all the learning that I received from the mistakes I made.

I wonder, if I live on, I will be of service to society? Do I have the stuff to make a positive impact on this world? I say: "Yes!" So, I soldier on, shaken or not.

January 24, 2023

3 A.M. POEM

Linda

Having loved,
Having been loved,
Having touched people's hearts,
Having been touched by people,
People mattered to me,
I mattered to them.
Without death,
Life isn't precious.
Not that I lived my life unregrettably, always
But I did my best under the circumstances.
I was given many blessings.

Chapter 4
Soldiering On

January 25, 2023

HAPPY BIRTHDAY!

Linda

I am 52 years old. Today is my birthday. I wake up feeling a sharp pain in my stomach and realize that I am hungry. And alive! A cold glass of oat milk sends me scurrying straight to the bathroom, though. On the other hand, I have this calm sense of having more energy this morning than on the previous several. It's my birthday, after all!

It's a miracle that this universe was created and that I was born into this particular world. How many things had to go right for me to find myself where I am? Yet a lot of things did, somehow, align perfectly to place me here where I belong. The earth came into being and provided the perfect conditions to host all living things to be born into it, live their lives, and finally pass on. I was born healthy, to a forty-year-old mother, her fifth and last baby. A poor woman in a country with no public welfare system (at the time) with a husband who was more accustomed to spending money than bringing it home. Did it ever occur to her: "How will I do this at all?"

I am told that my birth was initially not celebrated by my dad due to me being a girl. They had lost their previous child, a brilliant son, their best, to a childhood illness. Maybe they wished for another boy to offset their loss. A girl wasn't quite the same. Yet I turned out to be more. A vibrant, happy baby and child who won hearts by singing, dancing, and making witty and funny remarks (for my years, anyway). So, instead of regretting that I was not a boy, my family chose to adore me, the brat of the family. I was the youngest child, after all. I could get away with murder!

As a sensitive child, I was keenly aware of my mom's agonies and sorrows. Her marriage wasn't harmonious, and the back-breaking work she did to provide money for her kids' food and education took a toll. She never questioned her duty but it lay heavy on her – made worse by the fact that her husband just wouldn't accept his responsibilities or bring anything good home.

She would cry in front of a mirror (to this day, I don't know why in front of a mirror) and I assumed the role of consoler at the age of five. I started by singing her favourite psalms, then I'd share my vision of making something out of myself to provide a comfortable life for her when I grew up, then I'd hug her and chat with her until she calmed down. It worked – 100% of the time. She endured her non-partner until he passed away and then continued to do her absolute best to raise us kids.

So, on my 52nd birthday, here is my tribute to you, my dear mom.

DEAR MOM

Linda

Dear Mom,
You, the warrior,
Who wouldn't give your responsibility up for anything
Even if it meant working 20 hours a day, every day,
If it gave you bone aches,
You kept taking those harmful painkillers
Damn the long-term effects, you had your eyes on the prize:
You wanted to educate your kids so that they could live a better life
than you;
And we have, firmly lifted from poverty to middle class, thanks to you

You were born during the Japanese colonization,
Lived through World War II and the Korean wars
You saw it all and bore the brunt of unfair histories
Always, the poor take the worst
Through it all, you persevered
You did your best
And I might add
I made something out of my life and achieved my vision,
Because I promised you.
And if I hadn't fulfilled my commitment,
I wouldn't be your daughter, would I?

So today
On my birthday
I celebrate your life
I profess my undying love for you
You are long gone,
If there is another life,
I would still choose to be your daughter
this time however
You would be born wanting for nothing
A wonderful childhood with good education
Meeting a loving and devoted husband and father
Live a healthy life
Then you would die peacefully with your loved ones next to you

Mom...
If I can be only half as strong as you,
Cancer will be no match for me
So today on my birthday
I tell you, mom,
I'm a proud daughter of yours,
I am thankful for the life that you gave me
Well done, dear mom
Rest in peace

THE LITTLE BIRD

Håkan

Growing up in a country like Sweden where fairness and working for the common good are such strong values, this story really resonates with me. On days like these, it seems particularly apt:

A horseman is riding along a country road, and far up ahead he sees something lying smack-dab in the middle of the path. So he gets off his horse, walks closer, and realizes that it's a little grey sparrow, lying on its back, with his skinny little legs stuck up in the air.

Alarmed, the horseman asks: "Are you hurt, little sparrow?"

The little sparrow says: "No."

The rider asks: "Well then, what are you doing lying on your back like that for? I could have run you over!"

The little bird says: "Well, I heard the sky was going to fall today."

The horseman laughs: "And you think you can hold up the whole sky with your tiny little legs?"

And the little bird says: "We all do the best we can!"

To listen to the musical tribute to Linda's mom, check out:
https://hawkbjorn.com/time-to-go-home/

Chapter 5
A Good Cry

January 27, 2023

HITS AND MISSES

Linda

Here is the thing: we can accomplish almost nothing of value by ourselves. In other words, self-reliance (formerly a core value of mine) is often a delusion. We need each other to live and thrive in this world.

In terms of my cancer, I will need the medical expertise of others: assessments done right, the correct treatment strategy developed, then having this carried out skillfully. I will also have to rely on our friends, who now spend their weekends cooking nourishing meals to feed us during the week, and the social networks that are all part of our co-reliance.

We've been blessed with so much affection, encouragement, and support from our friends and families since we shared the news. Phone calls, emails, and food started pouring in almost immediately

– it seems that our loved ones have drawn up a schedule for who cooks for us, when – and we can taste the love that went into preparing it. We happily lean on everyone's care and generosity. You can practically feel how each of these kind acts weaves us closer together into a vibrant tapestry of give and take.

Speaking of food: I now have a permanently salty taste in my mouth. Right after I've eaten, this is joined by bitterness and intense sweetness, regardless of the food consumed. These three sensations are coarse and don't blend together well. It's like a persistent clanking noise, without any harmony or beauty to it. My taste buds have gone awry, like many other things in our lives right now. We all take things for granted when they go smoothly and complain when they don't. Simply being able to taste what you eat is such an underappreciated pleasure.

On the day after my first chemo treatment, I am scheduled for minor surgery. This involves putting "clips" (markers made of metal, each about 3 millimetres across) into the tumourous spots so mammograms and other non-invasive imaging tests can monitor them over time. After four months of chemo, when I go under the knife, these will also allow the surgeon to find the location of the original disease and determine if I'm winning.

The first radiologist didn't implant them all during my initial biopsy. Instead, he inserted two into nearby lymph nodes. His decision to not quite complete the job remains puzzling. Still, part of relying on others is trusting their professional judgment.

So, now I'm back on the hospital bed with local anesthesia about to be administered again. This time, they are going to place two more "clips" right into the tumours themselves. Then, I'll need to undergo more imaging to enable clear before-and-after comparisons that will let us see if the chemo is working.

...

Surprise! Another, seemingly more experienced doctor arrives, looks at the pictures, and determines that the markers are not where they should be. I'm going back on the operating table to renew my acquaintanceship with the large-bore biopsy needle, it seems.

The nurses and doctors begin to feel really sorry for me – apparently, these kinds of shenanigans aren't at all normal. I embrace their sympathy. I feel sorry for myself, too. Back on the same bed, with another needle and more markers going in, sorer than ever. That's when I lose it. I am exhausted, physically and emotionally. I shed quiet tears, then really start to sob when I finally see Håkan waiting for me in the car.

Good crying is what I needed! Not the kind that leaves you drained of energy but the kind that provides release. I can't always choose which one makes its appearance.

January 28, 2023

TRANSLATION: I CARE ABOUT YOU

Håkan

There are so many ways of expressing affection. A quiet hug, a knowing glance, a sweet poem, a pat on the back or a touch on the sleeve, a long, rambling, wonderful email, flowers, deliveries of comfort food, hopeful statistics ("There's an 86% survival rate!"), awkward silences and, yes, thoughts and prayers. It all adds up to a simple but powerful message: "I care about you!"

I haven't exactly shouted out our news at work but neither have I tried to hide it. People tend to be a little awkward about how to convey their emotions in this case, unsure of how their words will be received. A new colleague, upon running into me in the office kitchen, shows slight panic on his face – what to say, what to do? "Eeh, oh, eh, hi… Happy New Year! I mean, how are you? Eeh.. how are things going?" His consternation is replaced by a look of defeat and sorrow. I'm overwhelmed with empathy and the urge to hug him. So I say: "It's okay. It's fine. I hear you! Thanks for your sympathy and care. It really is appreciated!" I mean it and he looks relieved.

These past weeks have seen an outpouring of care, in all its forms. Often, these gestures are preceded by expressions of sorrow or apologies for not knowing what words to say. And, from my perspective, as the receiver of fond wishes, this is sweet, touching, humbling, and so very much appreciated. The sincerity shines through the ineloquence.

One family member does internet research. "I read that women who never had children are more likely to get breast cancer!" Linda's response: "Okay, so what do you want me to do about it?" A little late now, right?

But the "research" is not the point. The important thing is to realize that our bad news is truly upsetting to him. Because he cares, he needs to figure out his thoughts and feelings and tries to learn more. When he calls us the next day, he recites more information we already know. But these facts aren't what matters. Underneath all the noise, the message is loud and clear: "I care about you and I don't know how to say it and this whole thing is freaking me out!"

Another friend, bringing food over, exclaims: "So! You've got cancer! Well done!!" The shock of the statement throws us into hysterical laughter. Just what we needed!

This is a tough time for everyone, including well-wishers. It's hard to know what to say, how to act. So, we've decided to "subtitle" everyone who reaches out with different "I care about you" messages. This simply means that we immediately reciprocate their expressions of concern, showing them that these are appreciated regardless of any awkwardness they may feel.

Some of our loved ones share breast cancer survival stats; others tell us about their own aunt/mom/sister who also battled the disease. We've discovered that all attempts at expressing affection, no matter how awkward or imprecise, are welcome and worth embracing fully. Acceptance, courage, gratitude: these core values remain our compass.

An outpouring of support; an avalanche of kindness. There are so many ways to show these. And we know we are not alone.

Another colleague, an old-timer, finds herself alone with me at the end of a work-related video call. The agenda all done, we're both just quietly looking at each other, unsure of how to end the meeting. A few more seconds pass. I break the silence: "I can feel it. I feel your care. No need to say anything." Grateful nodding on the other side of the screen. Teary eyes. We wrap it up until next time. "Subtitling" the efforts of others really does work.

Chapter 6
The Three-Week Chemo Cycle

January 28, 2023

THANK THE SLEEP GODS AND YOU

Linda

Midway between two chemotherapy sessions, I wake up this morning feeling rested for the first time since Day One of chemo. Anyone who's had trouble with insomnia will appreciate the blissful embrace of sleep – when it finally comes for you. Sleep nourishes the soul, mind, and body. So, I'm grateful for having had a good night. Strengthened by that, we start our day with our usual morning routine: meditation and gratitude.

Dear Friend,
I am grateful for ....
You who chose to be present in my life,
By the universe's miracle, we met
Our souls connected,
Deeper than most
So we stuck around
Because we saw something that is
Rare and pure.

What I saw in you,
Your genuine heart,
Your sincerity about life,
And the levity that accompanies it.
Your quiet intellect,
Like your quiet charisma.
Your generosity drew me closer to you,
Because it is what I admire so,
You are a wise sage
Yes with flaws like everyone else
Because you are human.
It is your humanity, that is precisely why I fell for you.
Dear friend,
I am grateful for your presence in my life
Our past,
Our present,
And yes, why not our future?

On a very bright sunny day
I feel overwhelmed by your love and care

Your encouraging smiles,
Tears of empathy wanting to share my pain,
Careful questions,
Prayers,
I am blessed
By your presence.

Your devoted friend,
Linda

February 5, 2023

CHEMO-TERRIFIED

Linda

My first week of chemo was riddled with anxiety: the suspense of not knowing what to expect. What side effects are going to torture me? What remedies are available for each? How will the cancer cells in my body respond to treatment? The first day of chemo came and went and the unwanted, dreaded side effects showed up like ill-mannered guests: all kinds of sores, my tastebuds obliterated, digestive tract issues, skin trouble, headaches, nausea, and more. At least I know the devil now. One can always find an upside, even if this is only the awareness that something isn't actually worse than however bad it is.

Week two was packed with phone calls to the British Columbia Cancer Center, asking for the help of doctors, nurses, and pharmacists in wrestling with the side effects. Slowly but surely, the symptoms are responding to medication. I notice that we are being treated like royalty at our local pharmacy. I have a feeling that, by the end of this journey, I will be able to apply to be a pharmacist myself. I'm certainly throwing around terms like "dexamethasone" and "carboplatin" as if I've known them all my life.

Royalty I am, indeed! For the first time in my life, I have a direct line to a doctor, our oncologist. Also for the first time, several different professionals working at the BC Cancer Centre – nurses, specialist doctors, dieticians, a pharmacist and the nutritionist – are calling me periodically to make sure that I am alive and well. I'm impressed!

In an effort to distract ourselves from the many side effects assaulting my body, we've selected a few long-running Netflix series to help pass the time. One of these is *Downton Abbey*. I must say, I almost feel like I'm one of those aristocrats upstairs, encouraged to complain about whatever may be inconveniencing me. How's my sleep, how am I eating, how's my energy level, do I have any dizziness, any shortness of breath, any chest pain, how's my digestion, how are my fingers and toes (any numbness or purple discoloration), and so on.

Now, in the third week of chemo, my energy is almost back to normal. So is my appetite, despite my wacky taste buds. I'm deliberately fattening myself up to prepare for next week's chemo – I lost 3 kilograms after the first treatment (one can always find an upside…). I used to think that life without spicy food would be wretched; it turns out to be tolerable, all things considered. Right now, spiciness is just an unpleasant sharpness on my tongue. I have cut it out from my diet entirely and yet I am not entirely miserable. We live and learn! Håkan, on the other hand, keeps a little jar of crushed chilli peppers permanently on the dining table to stave off blandness.

Some side effects are more stubborn than others, requiring new medications, so our trips to our local, family-owned pharmacist continue. We enjoy showing them our friendship and loyalty. We could choose to go to a more convenient location and maybe enjoy slightly cheaper prices at some supermarket-sized emporium of pills, ointments, tinctures, powders, and sundry medical accessories, yet visiting our neighbourhood pharmacy gives us a feeling of familiarity that is very comforting in this unfamiliar cancer landscape. When you're standing on shaky ground, you hang onto anything stable. Plus, to Håkan's delight, they provide freshly popped popcorn to cheer up their customers, which it always does.

I was informed that the hair loss usually starts about now, and sure enough, I'm starting to shed like a German Shepherd. Picking up and cleaning my hair from around the house becomes part of the routine. It will be a week or two before I'm completely bald. We all hold dear certain images of ourselves and, when these start to conflict with reality, a slight panic sets in and we look for ways to hold onto that mental picture. Say we are getting older but continue to have a youthful self-image. Wrinkles show up, so we buy wrinkle creams. Our hair greys, we colour our hair. This is only partly because we care about how others see us; mostly, we're just not ready to give up the person we used to be.

I think back to those days when I panicked about discovering a small pimple or having a bad hair day (for which, of course, actually having hair is a prerequisite). There is such an over-emphasis on appearance. Aging has its own, unbending momentum and, with the passing of years, I've developed some objectivity and gotten much more relaxed about my looks.

Not that appearance is completely unimportant; it is a part of who we are. Our whole self is much more than our looks, though. Each of us can choose to see ourselves as either a body with a personality attached or a person who just happens to live in a body. Going by what you see online and in the media, the former seems to be the norm; this is a true shame.

The greater, better part of being human is an ability to forgive ourselves and others for our many deficiencies, physical and otherwise, to learn to see things from a broader perspective, to understand that nothing is really black and white and that the truth is so often multi-dimensional, and letting go, gracefully, when things are not within our control. Now, I live less in my own head and more as part of the universe. Understanding and recognizing our interdependence is what matters, taking us into a world beyond self-reliance. We can accomplish almost nothing of value by ourselves.

My rapidly balding head will soon force me to make a decision; I wonder about my next move. We've prepared head coverings of various sorts – a beanie, a scarf, and even wigs – to help ease the transformation. On the one hand, it is scary to think about this drastic and entirely involuntary change in my appearance. On the other hand, I can almost look forward to it, as a kind of evolution and progression.

Next week, we're back to Week One of the chemo cycle. I am told that it might be easier this time around, simply because I know what to expect now. I am also told that the chemotherapy gets progressively harder, and the side effects worse, with each dose. Maybe it will be both; that's just how life works sometimes. We encounter contradictions and imperfections at every turn. And how glorious is that!!??? Or is it? Yeah, it's both!

See you on the other side.......

February 10, 2023

LIFE IS NOT PERFECT

Håkan

Life simply isn't perfect: most of us learn this truth early in life; the rest end up suffering unnecessarily.. And, the longer we live, the more we discover just how rare perfection really is.

There is no ideal vacation, flawless partner, impeccable child, Utopian anything. In fact, imperfections surround us in pretty much every aspect of our lives and world. Now, this may sound a bit morose and depressing, but it doesn't have to be. Instead, we can see imperfections as liberating. We don't have to constantly compare ourselves and our actions to some kind of ultimate pie-in-the-sky ideal. We can fully admit that we sometimes need help, that we can't do it all alone. We can empathize when someone else doesn't rise to the challenge. We can begin to accept our deficiencies and our weaknesses for what they are: part of being human.

This doesn't mean we should stop trying to be better, of course. I would even say that imperfection does not give us the right to try any less hard. It also does not give us permission to "wing it", to "half-ass" it, to "good-enough" it. We still should strive to be our best selves, just with the realization that forgiveness is also available if we don't succeed every time. And certainly, imperfection never gives us an excuse to be cruel and unkind to others.

Life is not perfect, but it does go on. It means we can find freedom to live within our imperfections. And when we learn to fully embrace both beauty and weakness, we create the opportunity to live more fulfilled lives.

Chapter 7
Tears and Laughter

February 15, 2023

MEDITATING ON MY HAIR

Linda

The past five days have gone by in a blur. More chemo, more side effect management, more sleepless nights. Yet, after five long days and nights, grace and calm return. So does my energy. So, here I am, sitting upright, with my spirits up as well.

My hair has been falling out wholesale for the past two weeks.

Hair falling,

For days and days,

Like dry needles from pine and fir in the fall,

Ever so gently, yet wow, how much has fallen,

Making our living space an autumn garden

Some in clumps out from the comb,

Then into the trash bin that already hosts the earlier fallen soldiers.

Still enough attached to the head,

Hanging on for its dear life.

I wonder whatever for?

There are always hangers-on in our world:

People who won't quit while complaining about their relationships or work conditions, liberally and consistently,

People who hang on out of loyalty, even when it is not mutual

The truth is that hangers-on don't feel that they can be better off elsewhere. We will never know since we never give ourselves the opportunity to find out. Fear keeps us hanging on.

Settling for security or, even worse, less than I deserve, has never been my thing. I am a trained reader of bell curves, a useful skill when it comes to things like deciding whether to go into a booming market or leave a declining one. When any job or relationship starts to give us diminishing returns, we know that the curve has turned and, from there, there is only one possible direction. One can continue to ride the downward trajectory or leave.

Back to my hair loss: over the past two weeks, I have acquired a habit of continually picking hair off my clothes and floors. I think to myself how meditative this is.

The impermanence of hair.
The impermanence of our lives.
The impermanence of health.
This act of picking up hair, too, will soon cease.

Yet, it's exactly this impermanence that makes life so much more precious.

From the floor to the bin, then to the mirror

I see bald patches on my head.

My well-trained judgment reflex suggests the word "unsightly."

Still in a meditative state of mind, my better self counters: "Is it, really?"

From this perspective, it looks like it is "in transition".

I can dwell on the in-between mess that my scalp is currently in.

Or I can choose to get curious about my ever-changing look.

I see myself in the mirror now

For an instant, I look like a stranger,

Soon enough, though, I see my soul gazing back.

Equanimous, strong, and grounded

Hints of a smile even.

There,

All is good. I am here!

February 16, 2023

SIDE EFFECTS

Linda

Today, my stomach is acting up from who-knows-which drug; I took six different ones during the second chemo session. An overactive digestive system is one of the side effects of the treatment. I'm constantly hungry – growlingly, achingly hungry. I eat a bowl of soup and five minutes later my stomach is demanding more. This constant nagging for food is draining.

Saddled with a new back spasm and muscle aches in addition to acid reflux, the evenings start to challenge my wits. It's time to sleep now and we are lying face-to-face on our sides, trying to get control over the situation. My temperature is up, I am shivering, and my stomach is like an angry toddler screaming for attention. Whimpering softly, I fear that tonight is going to be no fun at all. Tears leak from my eyes. I don't need to cry as such but have to release the tension somehow. After a few sobs, calm sets in.

We decide on three measures – Tums, Tylenol, and a sleeping pill. We wait for them to take effect, which they do one after another. Shivers subside, then my lower back muscles stop straining against themselves. That is when we start laughing our heads off because of what Håkan just said: "My forehead is a tiny bit sore and my leg itches and nobody is paying attention to that!" We hold hands now, both curled up in our respective favourite sleeping positions.

I count my blessings starting with the obvious – you, my dearest, biggest blessing of my life, your levity, your eternal and unconditional love and yes, your patience.....and I drift into blissful sleep.

February 25, 2023

THE BUSINESS OF LIVING

Håkan

Our friends are constantly bringing us food – chicken noodle soup, rice cakes, Korean seaweed soup, dumplings; things that are easy to digest as well as relatively bland. This is so as to not upset Linda's suddenly delicate stomach – she used to be able to eat chili peppers as if they were apples.

I miss Linda's amazing cooking: fragrant, spicy, delicious dishes prepared with love, care, and skill. Of course, with her tastebuds carbonized by chemotherapy, she's now like a painter who has become colorblind. Or a singer who's lost her voice. Or, for that matter, a chef without her sense of taste and smell. Luckily for me, some of our friends also bring some dishes just for me – delicious chilli, spicy Ethiopian chickpea rice, roasted chicken, and so forth. I'm well looked after so that I can stay strong for her.

Aside from the emotional support Linda needs to help her deal with the rollercoaster of feelings induced by the chemo, there are also the practical aspects of everyday living to tackle. With Linda sidelined, I'm handling all the daily activities, taking care of the bills, responding to emails from well-wishers, organizing appointments and schedules.

Most of the people I deal with are very supportive and helpful. That said, with intense emotions swirling all around and a lot of new information to process, it's still a chore to try to react to this unfamiliar situation. Even the financial ramifications are daunting, like the loss of employment income, applying for a grant here, signing up for a prescription subsidy there, finding out whether or not our extended health insurance covers this or that, and on and on. It's all stressful. Filling out seemingly endless forms for Linda and booking various appointments: blood tests, CT scans, heart MRIs, more biopsies, echocardiograms, consultations with the reconstructive surgeon (as opposed to the breast cancer surgeon), radiologist, family doctor, nutritionist, more lab tests.

Considering the toll this is taking on me, I don't know how a beaten-up cancer patient can handle all of it on their own. Some patients, I hear, somehow manage it. A few even choose to go it alone, not wanting to "bother" anyone else. This can't be easy, though: imagine being too weak to get up for a glass of water or to go to the pharmacy for potentially crucial medication. I'm very happy to be "bothered".

Whether we're talking about getting married, becoming a parent, changing careers, or becoming seriously ill, coming to any major crossroads in our lives means making changes to our lifestyle. Cancelling our December hiking trip to Arizona seems like no more than a minor inconvenience now. Linda's plans to go and visit her mother's grave in South Korea for the first time – already delayed due to COVID and travel restrictions – can wait a while longer. We've got some idea of what's to come but we also know that nothing can truly prepare you for it. Our plan is just to take it one day at a time, deal with things as they arise, and remember to keep breathing.

Chapter 8
The Stories We Tell
Ourselves

March 1, 2023

LABELS

Linda

In our most recent meeting with our oncologist, a substitute doctor fills in for him during most of the appointment. As we discuss future treatment options, she mentions a fact we already knew but is nonetheless startling to us when stated in such an upfront way. She explains that the upcoming CT/PET scan I am to undergo will finally indicate whether my cancer is curable or not.

Essentially, if it has spread farther than we've all been hoping, beyond the lymph nodes, the cancer would be considered beyond the help of science. At that point, it could pop up anywhere, at any time in the future. Chemo, radiation, and surgery won't be able to catch up to it. Miracles do happen, but they're not to be relied on. It is quite an awakening.

This conversation also shows me something about human nature – well, at least mine and that of my loved ones. Although what she says is not exactly breaking news, we're shaken: we have already established one particular version of our future, based on the best possible scenario, in our minds. Without really thinking about it, we've just assumed that my cancer was stage 2 and that one year of treatment would almost certainly cure me.

How often do we create a story about ourselves and live in it as if that were the ultimate reality? What cherished illusions do we hold about our careers, relationships, talents, and dreams? In this case, the opposite possibility, which the doctor simply and straightforwardly laid out for us, was just another story and in fact just as likely.

Ever since this "revelation" of what we already knew, Håkan and I, in our separate heads, have been living in this new story as well as in our more favourable version. It's a strange kind of mental gymnastics: simultaneously entertaining both our hopes and our fears.

This got me thinking more about how we choose to characterize our identities. We casually label ourselves all the time: I'm a procrastinator, I'm lazy, I'm overweight, I'm a loser, and so on. These are self-limiting. Perhaps these labels were stamped onto us in our childhood by adults who didn't know better. Perhaps they come from experience – limited experience which we then extrapolated into a description of our entire being. In either case, they now form part of our stories – even if these exist only in our heads.

Of course, we apply positive labels as well – I'm smart, I'm a visionary, I'm a leader, I'm a doer… These self-affirming characterizations are supportive of growth, even when they're not entirely true. (Of course, flattering labels that are totally false can also be harmful. Convincing yourself that you're a great skier doesn't stop the laws of physics from applying to you.)

I've come across both kinds of stories in myself as well as while talking with friends and clients. So, each of our stories is defined by labels that are either self-restricting or self-expanding. The good news is this: we can change our labels when they're no longer useful or applicable, thus rewriting our stories of the past and future. We don't have to live with attributes that were given to us by others who may not have had our best interests at heart. We don't need to live out the stories they imagined on our behalf now that we're adults.

Am I still a procrastinator? The first question to ask is: "Have I always been? Was there a time when delay and hesitation weren't my default reaction to events?" This kind of self-examination can help guide us to revise counterproductive labels and thereby find ways to improve ourselves. Thinking of procrastination, we can probably think of past experiences where circumstances supported us in getting things done in a timely manner. Next time, we could say: "I'm an 'on-timer' and I have tools to help me."

THE VERDICT

Linda

Back to the divergent, vastly different stories held in my and Håkan's heads: on February 24, I had a CT/PET scan. The results took a few days to be interpreted. It turns out that…ready?

My cancer is indeed curable. By the time our doctor calls to share the good news, I am somewhat drained emotionally from the mental balancing act I've been attempting. I feel a bit taken aback instead of experiencing the sheer happiness one might have expected. Here I am, having just had years potentially added to my life, yet I don't feel like doing cartwheels. I barely even feel relief.

I think about my reaction afterwards. The worst-case scenario had already taken root in my mind. As often happens, I didn't create an alternate, better story to keep myself focused on the positive outcome. When we do come up with a favourable narrative, we tend to quickly disregard it, partly because of our self-applied, self-limiting labels. I wonder about the people who achieved great things: scaled Everest for the first time, put a computer in nearly every home, compiled the first encyclopedia, wrote symphonies that are still enjoyed today. Almost certainly, all of them experienced the normal human portion of self-doubt. What labels did they apply to themselves, though, in order to persist and succeed?

Giving up, of course, is always an option, though rarely the best one. With a plethora of unpleasant side effects to the chemo treatment showing up one after another, it occurs to me that the incurable scenario would have given me an out from these drastic methods of treating cancer, as irresponsible as this may sound to my loved ones.

Startling, eh? The usually strong Linda looking for an exit, an excuse to give up.

Speaking of my loved ones, Håkan's joy, relief, and happiness at the news has caused me to emphatically reconnect with the more pleasant narrative: one that describes my returning to health and living a long, "happily-ever-after" story with him. So, now I know I'm curable. No guarantees, yet the odds are good. With a bit of adjustment to my chemo dosage to help ease the side effects, we'll proceed with Chemo No. 3 today. The steroids that I've been taking from day one certainly bring me sleepless nights. So here I am, at 3 a.m., typing this – way too early and with a feeling of dread about the coming day and the days that will follow.

I remain sitting in front of the screen counting my blessings, expanding on the more pleasant story and diminishing my apprehension about what still lies in my future. I think about:

My loved ones: all together and each of them specifically, joining in my journey, supporting me and cheering me on.

My meditation practice: which has given me an equanimity that I couldn't have afforded otherwise during this time. Staying true to reality instead of getting lost in made-up stories, seeing things as they are, understanding the impermanence of all things, being present and enjoying each moment.

My appetite: aside from during the first week, I'm almost permanently hungry – often for food that I wouldn't normally crave. Towards the end of the chemo cycle, I'm eating just as much as usual, helping me to get back to my normal weight to better withstand the next chemical assault on my body.

Daily walks: my favourite activity to help me decompress, spend time in the fresh air, reconnect with nature, and be active. Håkan usually comes with me; we talk or just enjoy each other's company in silence.

My clients: the best patrons one can ever have, so accommodating and encouraging. They keep me grounded in my normal life and help me feel useful – how important this is to me (and, probably, anyone who's used to being self-sufficient) shouldn't be underestimated in a time like this.

My empathetic oncologist: he could have chosen to be a technician without empathy. His humanistic and caring heart makes a world of difference.

The whole medical support team: their earnest desire to help! I can feel their care right through the plexiglass. Bless them.

And so much more …

Despite the actions of some misguided individuals in this world, we are all intrinsically connected, not only with other human beings but with all things in nature. I'm blessed to be a part of it all. Along with this privilege, each of us bears a responsibility for doing our share to be a positive force. Improving the world, in whatever small way I can, also forms part of my story, which is now wholly uplifting.

It's still dark outside my window, but there is light just behind.

Much love!

Chapter 9
What's Fair?

March 27, 2023

CONFORMITY, MANNERS, JUSTICE, AND LUCK

Linda

Sometimes, when I'm confronted with someone's entitled behaviour, I recall this mental image of a little girl who doesn't get the toy she wants and complains with tears streaming down her innocent cheeks: "It's not fair!!!" In her world, fairness is about her getting what all the other kids got…but did they? All of them? Does each of them, in fact, want the same things?… What's fair is always relative and often difficult to define.

Growing up in a heavily male-dominated society, the concept of "fairness" (or rather, the lack thereof) often entered my thoughts. Typically, girls were sent to do chores while boys were allowed to play and laze around. When a woman kept giving birth to girls and failed to produce a son, it was somehow her fault. She was to blame even though, in biological terms, a baby's gender is determined by the father. Huh? Go figure!

Girls and women were also told not to "provoke" anyone of the opposite sex. If a man lost his cool and abused a woman, it was always the woman's fault. If girls were getting stares from men, the girls were at fault. So, yes, growing up, I was acutely aware of the word "fairness".

I remember standing in line for a bus ticket once when a man cut in line a few people ahead of me. When this happens, the "cut" is always in front of a woman since she wouldn't dare to challenge the man. I, being who I am, called him out. "Hey, sir, this is a line – and you might consider going to the back of it." He was visibly indignant at being reprimanded by a woman. "How dare you?!" he muttered, "Unlucky me, being scolded by a woman."

But the funny thing is that his predicament was caused by no one apart from himself, yet the fault was automatically the woman's. In his mind, it wasn't fair. He refused to budge because, as a man, he'd lose face. He couldn't do that. Soon, he was served by the ticket seller who was also a woman and didn't dare to challenge him. Events like these caused my sense of "fairness" to take root early and deeply.

Justice, in the legal sense, was also frequently lacking during the early decades of South Korea's democracy. I was acutely aware whenever it was nonchalantly ignored, when the powerful and connected used their influence without regard for the rights of others. Earlier in our lives, I noticed that Håkan had a much more relaxed attitude about fairness and justice. He never got as agitated about these issues as I would, even though he possesses a deep-rooted sense of right and wrong. Eventually, I concluded that this was because his life experience wasn't as full of inequity as mine had been. I, too, have gradually relaxed a little. After all, we've chosen to live in a society in which equity and equality are more of a norm.

So, it has been a while since I questioned what's fair. Is it fair that I have cancer? Cancer doesn't have much of an effect on my life most days, but the chemotherapy's side effects certainly do. The other day, I caught my mind complaining: "It's not fair." This startled and scared me. The underlying assumption was an interesting one: it insinuated that someone or something deliberately chose to harm *me*.

Here is the thing: life isn't meant to be fair. I'm not saying this from a place of defeat or implying that dog-eat-dog behaviour is okay. Rather, it's a recognition that happiness and fulfillment are more easily attained once we move away from the notion of "fairness". Most of the time, this whole concept is a product of comparison. Very often, comparisons only lead us to unhappiness and further from fulfillment.

It's just not useful to think in those terms – hoping for some abstract notion of justice to govern our lives doesn't bring us any closer to achieving the things that matter to us. Nor should we expect some mystical balancing force to make up for all the wrongs we've suffered in life. Instead, the rewards of handling these setbacks with good grace lie in greater maturity, wisdom, and compassion.

Nevertheless, we often find ourselves weighing our circumstances on the scale of "fairness":

Why didn't I get promoted (when others who haven't been with the company as long were)?

I work so hard, yet I have very little wealth to show for it (when others own so much more after spending less effort).

Why did I get diagnosed with cancer (when tons and tons of people with less healthy lifestyles remain free of it)?

What if we removed the comparisons (in parentheses) above and replaced them with honest and reflective questions instead?

Why didn't I get promoted? What do I need to do differently in order to be promoted next time? Am I in the right place for my own growth?

Why do I have so little wealth to show for all my hard work? I may work long hours, but am I using that time productively? Am I seeking the right advice in order to grow my wealth efficiently?

Why do I have cancer? Statistically, 1 in 8 women in North America will be diagnosed with breast cancer during their lifetime. So, why not me? Instead, I choose to be glad that seven other random women are safe from my bad luck. I think of seven women in my own life I love and care about and crack a smile.

Life presents all sorts of situations, fair or not. And it's rarely perfect. If we can move beyond comparisons and embrace both the beauty and imperfection of life, we create the opportunity to live victoriously in both.

March 31, 2023

FEISTY FIVE

Håkan

Linda has now undergone her fourth chemo treatment. She has two more to go before surgery, and we're starting to sense patterns. The first few days after all those infusions, her whole body is feverishly warm, her face flushed, and she's very tired and listless. Once a week has gone by, the dreaded side effects emerge prominently – nausea, headaches, an elevated temperature (though this was only after the first round of chemo), serious hives (after the second), aches all over, indigestion, sore eyes, weird metallic tastes in her mouth, and so on. The third week is much better – her body bounces back from the onslaught of the poisons, she recovers, sleeps well, her appetite improves, and we enjoy a period of calm before the next storm settles in.

We humans love patterns. Our brains detect them in order to make sense of the world and to share that understanding with others. Patterns create some semblance of order even when they exist only in our minds. Think of clouds. We see things – a whale, a face, a figure, a dog chasing a ball – instead of just the swirling white vapour that's actually there.

So, here's a new pattern that I've discovered. I call it the "Feisty Five". On day five after the chemo treatment, her exhaustion dissipates, the fog lifts, and my no-longer-passive Linda comes roaring back. This is the one I fell so completely and helplessly in love with many years ago. The fiery, energetic, always active, "ants-in-her-pants"

Linda that I adore. The one who takes me on the most amazing adventures around the world and in our imaginations. The one who almost bought a 40-acre macadamia nut farm on Hawaii's Big Island in 2011. The one who did buy roughly 5 kilograms of peaches just minutes before a two-hour walking tour of Zagreb because they looked tasty. The one who challenges me to be a better human every day.

Today is day five and it's a little foggy.

Me: *"Look at the mist moving across the lawn!"*

Linda: *"It's not moving. The wind is moving it. The wind is the owner of the movement!"*

Ha! Feisty Five. She's back. And I'm so happy! One kiss on the cheek is all I need. And I'll carry a backpack full of fruit for you any day.

Chapter 10
Love & Friendship

April 2, 2023

LASTING AND TEMPORARY ATTACHMENTS

Linda

Some friendships are enduring, steady and solid. We are powerfully connected. Genuine love glows in our midst, all the time. Even if we don't see each other for a while, we know in our hearts that our friendship is fulfilling and profoundly satisfying. We agree on most things and, even when we don't, we've got each others' backs.

Other friendships are somewhat secondary to the main current of our lives. Unless events or specific needs bring us together, there is this tentativeness about them. It's like canned food that we picked up with every intention to use but which got shelved and is now gathering dust in the cupboard. One day, perhaps, a new recipe is discovered and this particular can of beans will come in handy. It may even turn out to be exciting.

The pervasive tone between most acquaintances, though, is hesitant and non-committal. I've never been keen on shelved friendships. Is it because I am Korean? My understanding of the culture is that we value and treat "real" friendships as something on par with family bonds or, often, even more important than blood relations. Maybe, this view is just a product of my core values and preference for having deeper, more connected relationships.

We all hold on to some friendships that were formed mainly because we were in the same place at the same time. We may have been allies at school or work, great colleagues, or even mentors and mentees. When the environment changes, some relationships don't endure: they're only capable of thriving in fertile ground. Life moves on and so does the friendship – we need new allies to suit our new environment.

While meditating, I often observe my mind dwelling on these past relationships. Sometimes, it is with a sense of loss and even a hint of resentment. Nothing is permanent and I accept the transient nature of things. Peace envelops me once more as I remind myself of this. So, dear ones, once close, now no longer: may you find nurturing soil, surrounded by companion trees that support and cheer your growth, and may you receive lots and lots of sunshine.

Then I get overwhelmed by the love for the friends we have in our lives right now. Sincere hearts that I connect with through chats, Zoom calls, and in person, from whom I have received so much support during this cancer journey. How blessed I feel to have these people by my side, whether located near or far. Their genuine care for us pulses like a heartbeat, steady and regular. So present, so life-sustaining and affirming. It has been a long-time routine for Håkan and I to contemplate gratitude right after our morning meditation. I count my blessings and I send my appreciation for our friends into the universe.

April 10, 2023

POCKETFUL OF CHERRY BLOSSOMS

Håkan

I picked a pocketful of cherry blossoms on our Saturday after-lunch walk intending to sprinkle them around the house. I then promptly forgot them in my pocket, only to discover them again on our after-lunch walk the next day and return them gently to their buddies on the ground. So, our weekend: well, there was happiness (picking cherry blossoms), then a little sadness and embarrassment (finding the blossoms again, now a bit browned and wrinkled), and then, oddly, satisfaction and closure (returning them to the swirling, beautiful "snowfalls" under the rows of cherry trees).

A weekend of near-perfection and intrusive imperfection. Like most of our lives. The trick is to give our full attention to the cherry blossoms and the blue sky.

April 17, 2023

CONNECTED

Håkan

With the fifth round of chemo steadily working its way through Linda's body, we are now contemplating the remaining trials to come. She has one more chemo session to go, to be followed by surgery on May 30 and radiation therapy later this summer.

In the best possible scenario, Linda will "only" need intravenous drug therapy for the remainder of this year: a simple infusion every three weeks with no major side effects. Alternatively, if residual cancer is found lingering in her body, she may require another nine months of combined chemo/drug therapy. We will only know which is the case once the doctors have studied the pathology report from the surgery. No matter which scenario we face, anything will be easier than the current chemo regime (relatively speaking, anyway).

So, stuck in limbo, we plan ahead in hope. We'd rather be optimistic until we're wrong instead of dreading the worst until we're right.

Living and thinking this way can be difficult, sure: it's like we're all programmed to spend more time countering potential threats than embracing opportunities. Even so, always assuming the worst can only prevent you from leading a fulfilling life.

In this fleeting yet epic journey we call living, we continually learn, adjust, reassess, evolve. We are constantly on the move, even when we sit still. The earth spins us into the future with time ever ticking, adding up the minutes, hours, days, and years we've been gifted to be here with each other. And we are all connected, like the ocean and the sky.

That's what love does: connect us. That's why we live together in families, communities, villages, cities, and countries. That's the reason whole societies are built. Love is why we prepare food for each other. That's why we make things that improve our comfort. That's why we write songs. That's why we smile at those we know. And sing together. That's why we go to work. Really, we grind away in our little cubicles or rice fields because we don't want to spoil this love we carry for one another. Oh, occasionally we break down, through selfishness or ignorance, yet as horrible as we can be to each other, this world really is a work of love… it hums along because we love, not because we hate.

It hums along because we love…our mothers, our brothers, our friends, co-workers, our countries, and lovers, our gods, our home villages and cities, our fellow humans, this beautiful planet…it all works because we love.

We are all connected. Like the ocean and the sky.

Chapter 11
Choices We Make, Choices We Don't Make

April 24, 2023

OBVIOUS AND HIDDEN OPTIONS

Linda

Now, with only one chemo treatment left to go, I think about the choices Håkan and I will need to make soon. If no cancer cells remain in my body after the surgery, it will be called a "complete response" and things are definitely looking up. If a few (or perhaps more than a few) have escaped the chemo drugs, we'll be looking at "residual disease". This is obviously less than ideal, but it would not necessarily mean disaster.

It seems like the oncologists and radiologists may recommend radiotherapy regardless, although I am given the choice to forego radiation if the result is a "complete response". The doctors' main objective, in this case, is to ensure that no cancer is present and prevent any cancerous cells from showing up again. That means radiation, even though this comes with its own set of risks. Without it, even a complete response may see cancer returning afterward.

My main goal, aside from beating cancer, is to minimize invasive measures, thereby reducing side effects and any long-term damage to my body while remaining cancer-free. This seems simple enough, but the options are complex and difficult to quantify.

Naturally, I start thinking about choices more generally.

There are a lot of events in our lives that we can consider "decisive" moments. Some people may not even realize that they have a choice. For them, being forced to decide between two or more alternatives can be paralyzing. That's not me. I've always embraced choices; options, for me, mean freedom.

We can choose to retire at age 45. A lot of people don't consider that a possibility. Society dictates a defined retirement age, so this "choice" is only recognized as such once you're almost over the hill.

We can choose not to subscribe to the absurdities of the rat race and instead construct a life that is harmonious and life-affirming, not only for ourselves or even just our fellow human beings but for all living things. This is what I did when I left my high-paying corporate job, and I've never had more than a few moments of regret.

We can choose not to be offended even though someone said something insulting. We can choose to view these comments in the context of their own life histories rather than ours.

We can choose to buy a BMW and gain so-called prestige, or we can choose to unsubscribe to the idea of purchased status. We can embrace the idea that everybody's opinions about us don't matter equally and instead focus on earning the respect of the people we care about.

We can choose to deprioritize a very long-standing relationship that is no longer serving us because we are now walking separate paths, experiencing different things, and have evolved to be incompatible.

Choosing requires energy. Weighing the benefits and disadvantages of various options requires mental effort; psychologists even use the term "decision fatigue". Choosing requires empowerment. Without a sense of having control over your environment, choices don't seem real. Choosing requires responsibility. We need to accept the consequences of our decisions. Often, not choosing is a heck of a lot easier. We blame others instead, even though remaining passive is just as much a decision as doing something.

Along this cancer journey, Håkan and I have made more than a few important choices.

We decided to go on the chemotherapy program despite all the possible consequences. The odds of surviving cancer are significantly higher with chemo, and that was our main consideration. We chose my life over death.

That said, I did think about the possibility of foregoing chemo. It seems to me that simply prolonging the same life that I have always lived would be a little redundant; merely a chance to experience the same things all over again. But I referred back to my life purpose: "Doing good by guiding people to their intentional and fulfilling lives and improving the lives of others through philanthropy." Well, considering that I can be a positive force in this world, it's kind of my responsibility to survive. So I chose to increase the odds of life once I contemplated my future impact on the world.

Here's the thing: I don't want to just live for a long time. I want to live healthily and actively – until I drop dead. I'm afraid of having to struggle on saddled with the long-term health problems chemo and radiation treatments sometimes result in. With sore muscles and numbness in different parts of my body now a daily fact of life ever since Chemo No. 4, I mull over the long-term consequences of accepting radiation on top of chemo treatments and surgery. A human body can only take so much. We'll need a bit more information before making our next choice.

> *"Life is a matter of choices, and every choice you make makes you."*
>
> —John C Maxwell

April 26, 2023

AVOID CHAOS AT ALL COSTS

Håkan

We yearn for certainty; a kind of security. "What is the meaning of life?", we want to know, hoping for a simple answer.

We strive hard for stability. Surround ourselves with structure. Avoid chaos at all costs.

But life is like a windstorm that swirls and tugs at the branches of trees, ripples the water on the ocean, creates discombobulated clouds in the sky, ruffles tall grasses into disorganized swaying.

Let go. Bend with the wind. Go with the flow. Sway with the music.

There are no guarantees in life. Only moments of joy, pain, laughter, sadness; love, and hate, too. But nothing bigger than love. Bigger than the ocean and the sky put together. Love has no limits.

May 3, 2023

PARTNERING WITH PROFESSIONALS

Linda

The past couple of chemo treatments brought on some extraordinarily bad side effects. This alerted us that we need to reduce the dosage of one chemo agent and drop the other entirely for my last session. We asked the doctor if this would affect the efficacy of my treatment and he said it won't. This topic has come up before and the reasoning always puzzles us. If a lower dosage doesn't affect the result, why do we have to go with the maximum in the first place?

My understanding of the answer is that, as long as a body can tolerate it, doctors will just keep throwing more treatment at it to maximize the chances of winning the battle. Dosages go up when they can; down if they must. It is always a risk-versus-reward decision.

Even today, medical technology has not reached the sophistication necessary to detect cancer cells at a microscopic level (unless you cut open every part of your body and put it under a microscope, which isn't practical even for autopsies). A good analogy for chemotherapy is shooting as many bullets as you can at the enemy hiding in the undergrowth because you can't see all of them, then hoping for the best. The problem is that you are killing your own soldiers at the same time. I find the latter part troubling.

Normally, this lack of clarity in my decision-making would bother me. I'm used to being able to call on figures, charts, and financial statements that have a very small margin of uncertainty. However, my life has also taught me that we need to effectively partner with the professionals we hire instead of leaving all of the decisions up to them. They possess expertise in their fields, of course, but we alone truly understand our wants and needs.

The only way to make a rational choice is to harmonize both viewpoints. For the doctors, in this case, destroying the cancer without killing the patient is the win they're looking for and everything else is secondary. This may simply be the attitude their training fosters. I, on the other hand, treasure my life only up to a certain point. If some treatment will leave me too feeble to live out my remaining years enjoyably and effectively, it's just not a good option.

Håkan and I have also sometimes run into trouble because the "professionals" we hired weren't always competent or fully committed to their customers' success. A few professions, at least anecdotally, are more guilty of this than others, like (some) mortgage loan brokers, realtors, financial advisors, insurance salesmen, and so on. At times, we got bad results even when they did their best. This, if you know me, is something that I can forgive compared to if they simply slacked off or didn't care how things turned out, which is far less excusable.

I have encountered this in the medical field, too. About 20 years ago, I had a breast biopsy. Yes, that's true! Way back then, I had a kind of foreboding of what was to come. Instead of examining the left breast, as requested, the doctor did the biopsy on the right. I ended up going through the same procedure twice as a result. Back then, this didn't mean just using a needle, as is common today, but was instead rather invasive and involved general anesthesia and surgical knives.

I was stunned at the possibility of a medical professional making such a mistake. Later, however, I realized that doctors are human too and nobody is perfect all of the time. Why the procedure went wrong, I wouldn't know. Another doctor was standing in that day for my usual specialist. What surprised me was that the doctor who slipped up called me in the evening to apologize. She was truly sorry and rattled too. "How do we ensure that this doesn't happen to other patients?" is what I asked. After their reassurance that this would be looked at across the system and rectified, I forgave them.

I wondered, though, how I could have partnered with this particular team. Should I have asked more questions? Been more involved? When dealing with a complicated, specialized field like healthcare, however, giving your trust to a professional always entails some risk. It's not like recommendations or online reviews by laymen can tell the whole story.

So, even though my doctors know much more about my disease and treatments than I do, I recognize that I need to take an active part in the decision-making process so we can make better choices together. Fortunately, they encourage or at least tolerate my many questions and "meddling". I'm usually a team player but, when it comes to cancer, I find meaningful collaboration difficult. So much is unknown, not just to me who is still new to all this but also to the specialist oncologists.

What are the statistics regarding undergoing only five sessions of chemo instead of six? How does this impact my chances of beating the cancer? Since this is not an option given to patients unless they can't physically tolerate the final infusion, we don't have enough data to know one way or the other.

What dosage of a specific chemo agent is appropriate for someone of my weight, my ethnicity, my diet, my age, etc.? There are so many variables and not enough stats to rely on. When there is reliable information to hand, it empowers doctors and, yes, patients as well. With cancer, a lot of data is out there in general terms, yet the nature of statistics makes it hard to apply this in a specific situation.

So, what's the best course forward? I'll trust my doctors' experience and their best intentions to help me cure the disease and thrive in my life afterwards. I go back to my value of "acceptance" once more, one of those I'm trying to embrace more thoroughly as part of my cancer journey.

Chapter 12
Passing a Milestone

May 3, 2023

THE LAST CHEMO

Linda

The nurse is very aware that my last chemo session is today – this time around, at least. She congratulates me. I am thankful for her acknowledgement of this milestone. How many patients has she seen passing through her care; how many stories must she have to tell? How much hope and encouragement must she have shared over the years?

More broadly, I am extremely grateful to be at the end of this chapter of my cancer treatment journey. I'm saying this prematurely, of course: the next few weeks, until the chemo has worked its way out of my body, will still be hard. Nonetheless, we mark the event anyway. Telling myself and my loved ones that this important landmark has been passed and celebrating it together is meaningful. It's one way to break a very long, exhausting trek into bite-sized stages and make each more achievable and manageable. When it comes to finding the will to keep going through the rough patches, perception is everything.

Milestones are hugely motivating in our life journey. Imagine running a marathon without any landmarks. You know that you need to cover 42.195 kilometres but there are no distance markers or water stations along the way. There's no one cheering you on from the side of the road. You have no idea how far you've come or how far you have yet to go. Unless you brought your own map, you may not even know that you're still going in the right direction. That kind of run will be significantly harder and perhaps hopeless, even though the total distance is the same.

So, in our lives and businesses (I mention this since I'm a business coach), we set milestones for ourselves. Each represents a specific accomplishment on the way to actualizing our big vision – the finish line in each of our personal marathons. We can tell our brain and body that we only have a few more kilometres to cover till we reach the next milestone. Running the whole distance is one long exercise in drudgery; covering just 4.22 km – even ten times in a row – is easy by comparison.

So, we create pragmatic milestones to guide the course of our lives:

I'd like to be a sales manager in two years so that, eventually, I can become a sales director.

I will make the downpayment on my first investment property in the next two years in order to, one day, establish a real estate portfolio; my final goal is to fully support my lifestyle from passive income by my early forties.

I'm going to lose 1 pound every 6 months so that I'll end up fit and feeling more confident about my looks.

My cancer journey has also had a few milestones along the way: all six of the "hard" chemo infusions (I call it this as I may have to undergo another, less harsh course of chemotherapy if the doctors don't see a complete response), surgery, radiation, and more targeted drugs…and, possibly, additional treatments we currently don't know about. All of these are or can be marked on my personal calendar. I try to see them as breakthroughs to celebrate instead of events to be dreaded.

Today, the first major milestone has been passed. We asked a few friends to join us for a dinner out to mark the occasion last night. (It's entirely possible that my appetites for both food and social interaction aren't going to be enormous right after a chemo infusion.) It also happens that yesterday was our 25th wedding anniversary!

Who would have expected that our journey together would include a battle with cancer? Yet, we always knew that, regardless of whatever adversity we'd encounter in our joined lives, we would be there for each other. So, here we are – our partnership stronger than ever, more certain than ever, as it is so deeply rooted in our shared experience of overcoming life's challenges as well as savouring its joys and happiness, together.

I also want to share my heartfelt gratitude with the people who have walked this journey with us so far. We are so touched by your generosity and kindness. The world is a better place because of you and we are strengthened by your encouragement.

Cheers to you,
Linda

May 4, 2023

WAKING UP

Linda

I wake up a little too early this morning – still too dark to start the day just yet. So, I stay in bed and just let my mind wander, presenting a smorgasbord of various images and conversations, some in the past and some in the potential future. Then, I watch as daylight spreads slowly and gradually like ink blotting on a piece of paper. Birds of different kinds start their days busily communicating whatever is important to them – some as loudly as they can, others much more subtly.

In his book Waking Up: A Guide to Spirituality Without Religion, Sam Harris says: *"How we pay attention to the present moment largely determines the character of our experience and, therefore, the quality of our lives."* There are circumstances and the way we choose to perceive them; arguably, the nature of our perceptions matters more.

When we switch off our mind's default "autopilot mode" and start observing our passing thoughts as if they were someone else's, we give ourselves a break. It's the moment that the spell is broken and our minds exist as they were meant to. By allowing the mind a bit of distance between it and our thoughts, we give it a far better chance of coming to more balanced interpretations. It's like the difference between being caught outside in a hailstorm and calmly watching it through your living room window.

In our daily lives, we are all presented with various challenges and opportunities. How do we see and interpret them? How do we respond to these interpretations? Every one of us likes to think that we are rational beings. Yet, when you observe the actions of those around you – and, perhaps, your own thoughts – you quickly realize that we don't actually respond to facts and events but to our understanding of them. Interpretations matter a great deal.

I have cancer. On autopilot mode, my mind would be making up a story of a victim, with me in the starring role: "I'm extremely unlucky and everything is against me." My interpretation could be that this whole deal is unfair considering that I have always led a reasonably healthy lifestyle. "Why me?"

Or, I could catch myself and alter the course of my mind's trajectory. I can then choose to see that my unfortunate situation is the result of random odds, a roll of the dice that didn't go my way. Moving on, I can use this as an opportunity to expand in a direction that wasn't available to me before. So far, this journey has allowed me to do just that. I've connected with family members and friends in a way that wasn't previously possible. I've learnt to rely more on others and to be more vulnerable. Acceptance is easier now than before. Going at a different pace, a slower one, allows me to explore different viewpoints and has given me a new appreciation for everyday scenery. It's just like how walking around in an unfamiliar city gives us access to a level of detail that we are unable to experience while driving around those same streets.

I also live with a new awareness of the impermanence of life and accept this as part of my reality, more so now than I ever did pre-cancer. I'm a lot less attached to things, the status quo, and even some people as a result. I knew that four months of chemo would end one day, and now the last round is making its way through my system. I know that I'm scheduled for major surgery at the end of the month and that the subsequent six weeks of recovery will probably be very unpleasant. But I also know that this, too, will pass. Eventually, one day, the whole treatment program will be behind us. As trying as this experience has been, we will emerge stronger in the end.

Death is no longer a scary monster. It will come sooner or later regardless of what interpretation I attach to it. I'm even more convinced now than ever that we need to live an intentional, deliberate life. It's so short that we don't have the luxury of time to squander.

Having been confronted with the notion of my life ending, I am cognizant of what counts and what doesn't in the end. People whom I care about count. The positive impact that I can make on the people around me counts. What I strongly believe in, and living accordingly, count. Now matters much, much more than later.

What doesn't count? Material stuff doesn't. Social status doesn't. Relationships that are no longer fulfilling to both parties don't. Success doesn't, unless it's accompanied by improving the lives of others in some way. Beyond a certain minimum, the contents of your bank account certainly doesn't.

Our quality of life resides in the presence of our minds. The relationship we have with our minds determines all the other relationships we have in our lives: with people, with things, and with ideas.

So I listen to the birds, I watch the sunrise, and my mind is awake.

Chapter 13
Trusting the Universe
(Surgery Day)

May 30, 2023

TWO FOR ONE

Linda

We have two surgeons: one is called a breast surgeon, a specialization I didn't know existed before all this. I mentioned our initial meeting earlier: she is very highly regarded in her field but doesn't exactly go out of her way to show her patients empathy. Taking out the tumoured part of my left breast is her responsibility.

The second one is a plastic surgeon who will reconstruct the breast after the first removes the tumour and surrounding tissue. Cramming two surgeries into one session means the procedure will be rather long. We'll have to get an early start: at 6:30 a.m., a doctor at a different hospital is supposed to take care of the sentinel nodes – the lymph nodes to which the cancer spread first. Then, after a short drive, I'll be admitted to the hospital where my breast surgeon practices. This is where the two surgeons will scrub up, one after the other, to complete the procedure.

Starting in April, Håkan, I, and various doctors started discussing our options for reconstruction. Should we even bother and, if so, to what extent? We learn two more medical terms: lumpectomy (partial removal) and mastectomy (full removal) of a breast. What we decide will determine the nature of the reconstruction. We can choose between using a silicone implant or my own skin. At this point, we learn several more technical words, which I won't repeat here. You don't need to know them until you need to know them.

Would opting for a lumpectomy rather than sacrificing an entire breast increase the chance of the disease spreading? Would it also mean that I'll have to get radiation to improve the odds of long-term survival? The side effects of radiotherapy are supposed to be less extreme than those of chemo; even so, I've had enough of those to last me a lifetime.

After some further consultations, we decide on a lumpectomy, which is way less invasive and requires a much smaller surgery (in terms of both the taking out and filling in parts). We're told that this does not reduce the odds of survival. It seems to us that this is clearly the winning choice: the less tissue is removed from the breast, the less tissue needs to be taken from another part of my body to replace it, and the easier it should be to recover from the operation.

One of my friends jokes that some people pay to get their breasts augmented. In this case, it's free and I should take advantage of it. In fact, I was offered the choice of retaining my original size or ending up with a bigger or smaller bust, even though it will only be a lumpectomy. We are not discussing my bra size here and I will leave out the details of my choice. Another decision to make, though at least this one was easy.

SOCIETY'S FOCUS ON APPEARANCE

Linda

Some of us choose to be highly attentive to how we look – either in the eyes of others or to ourselves – and some of us prefer to care less. And many of us have attitudes that fall somewhere in between the extremes.

I was an international student at the University of Melbourne, in Australia, from 1995 to 1996. I hung out with other international student friends, mainly Singaporean and Indonesian, in the postgraduate centre as well as in the nearby open-air Victoria Market. We'd often meet up in the latter for coffee or lunch. One day, we were lounging in the sun drinking our cappuccinos and noticed two girls walking towards us, about 50 meters away. One of my Singaporean friends remarked: "I bet they are Korean." This surprised me and I asked why. He said that his guess was based on their makeup and the way they carried themselves.

I realized then how pervasively we wear the masks that society imposes on us. "This is how girls and women should look," everyone from our parents to magazine editors delight in telling us. I realized that I was wearing the same kind of make-up as these two strangers. Suddenly, I started questioning my own attitude to fashion and self-presentation. This was not because I dislike the Korean look but rather because I was surprised at my unquestioned, unexamined acceptance of it for myself. In this respect, at least, I was living by default, not according to my own design. I was subscribing to a certain set of social norms not because they suited me but because I'd always done so…and because everybody else was doing the same thing.

I asked myself why I wore makeup: just because. From this moment of recognition, I slowly but surely started to form my own ideas about beauty. What kind of women do I see as role models? What is it that I admire about them?

The drawback of defining your own standards of beauty is that you may end up looking "attractive" in your own eyes even though most other people don't find the way you look appealing (or even, perhaps, respectable). Now, if I can live with the fact that I may not be a walking embodiment of their ideal of beauty, this isn't much of a problem. I happen to place less emphasis on outward appearances than many others do.

Another recognition that affected my approach to good looks is this: whose opinions matter in our lives? If a certain contingent of men don't think I am attractive, should I care? Then, the question comes down to "What kind of men do I admire? What do they look for in their partners?"

If augmented breasts are your thing, then you are not my thing.
If feminine means wearing makeup, you're not my kind of masculine.
If your topics of conversation regularly revolve around appearance, you are not my crowd,
…and so on.

You can derive a lot of confidence from knowing that each of us still has plenty of people who see us as attractive, inside and outside. We don't need the admiration or approval of the whole world for us to feel desirable, only a small circle of people who share similar values.

I DON'T KNOW MUCH

May 30, 2023

Håkan

I know how to write songs. I know how to give presentations to large groups of people. I know how to drive a stick shift and on the left side of the road, which is useful when we're travelling in Australia/NZ/UK. I know how to make pickled herring. I even know how to whistle. But I have no idea how to surgically remove cancer cells from Linda's body.

So, this morning at 6:30 a.m., we stop first at St. Paul's Hospital for a sentinel node infusion (I don't even know what that is). Later, as I drop Linda off at Mount St. Joseph's Day Surgery, I feel rather helpless. And thankful at the same time. It's a weird, ambiguous combination of anxiety, inadequacy, relief, nervous energy, and immense gratitude.

I'm grateful that we can lean on this team of highly trained individuals who have dedicated much of their lives to learning how to find cancer cells hiding inside human bodies, who know how to properly administer anesthesia, who know how to stitch incisions and dress wounds, who know how to reconstruct body parts and move blood vessels and all kinds of other things most of us have no clue about. So, there's that. And my blurry feeling of gratitude and helplessness.

Aaron Neville said it best:

"I don't know much but I know how to love you. And that may be all I need to know".

June 1, 2023

FLOATING

Linda

"Take a deep breath in, then let it out. Take a few more deep breaths, in and out." These are the instructions I get from the anesthesiologist. By my third breath, I think, I am asleep like a baby. Six hours later, I am woken up by someone calling my name. There are no surgeons in sight and no giant lights above my head. I'm in the recovery room.

My day starts just after dawn at the Nuclear Medicine Department of one hospital, then we drive to a different hospital for the surgery. After what seems like half a lifetime of waiting, I am moved to the operating room at 12:30 p.m. When Håkan picks me up, it is after seven in the evening. It was one giant long day, even if I was unconscious during a lot of it. Without any debriefing from the surgeons, which seems a bit odd, we're left to assume that the surgery must have gone as anticipated.

Walking out of the hospital into the chilly, sunny evening with Håkan's hand steadying me, I feel like a stranger in an alien city. The triple whammy of anesthesia, nerve blockers, and painkillers certainly makes me feel like I'm not walking on solid ground; it's more like I'm floating along above the pavement. Still, another milestone has been overtaken. What a sense of relief I feel when thinking about this!

In the car on our way home, we talk about all the sweet and sincere well-wishes and messages that we received over the past few days from our friends and families. We're overwhelmed by such love and generosity. And truly blessed.

I'm now recuperating, taking it one day at a time. No major pain, no troubles so far. Just stiff, groggy, and in need of rest. Next week, we'll meet with the surgeons and find out more about what comes next on this journey of illumination. Thanks for keeping us company. It's so good to know we're not walking alone.

June 6, 2023

FORGING CONNECTIONS

Linda

Today, we have appointments with our two surgeons – two separate meetings in two different buildings; no "two-for-one" deal this time. The first meeting, with the breast surgeon, is typically "clinical" and somewhat dispassionate. It lasts only a few minutes: she gets right down to business. No "nice to see you", "how are things?", or smiling chit-chat. Just the facts. "You're healing well and I don't need to see you again." That is it. Strangely, afterwards, I think I must need a bit more time with her, someone with whom I just shared the biggest challenge of my life. This abrupt ending is a bit unsettling. I find my reaction strange, because I don't see myself as "needy" or all that dependent on other people.

The meeting with our reconstruction surgeon makes for a stark contrast and is many, many degrees warmer. She is also happy with my healing progress. And shares, to our surprise, that both she and the usually aloof breast surgeon came to see me as I was waking up from the anesthesia to let me know that the surgeries had gone well. She mentions that about half of their patients remember these conversations while the other half don't. I'm obviously in the latter category.

Apparently, the nerve blocker that they administered can induce a short-term amnesia effect. It is given to reinforce the effect of anesthesia while reducing the necessary dosage. I am strangely and retroactively thankful that they visited me after the surgeries. I've been observing a change in myself: I tend to look for reasons to be grateful, all the time. This, I say, is a BIG thing. A gift from my cancer journey: finding out (again) that gratitude is always an option.

The surgeon shares her warmest smile when seeing us off. She says I don't need to worry about anything, but focus on healing. Right, she also mentions the exercises that I need to do to help my arm and shoulder heal properly and regain their normal range of motion. We will see her again next week. This, surprisingly, comforts me perhaps more than it should – it is just a doctor-patient meeting, after all. Yet, knowing that our relationship is not yet at an end somehow reassures me.

I think about the place empathy has in this world. Many, many years ago, I attended a six-month training program on cross-cultural counselling at UBC Continuing Education. One of the very first skills we learned in the course was "empathy". Expressing this, in a coaching context, is surprisingly simple. You simply hear about a client's situation and offer a statement in return:

"I have so much to do and so little time."

You must be frustrated.

"I don't eat much but even water seems to add weight to my body."

You must feel confused and upset.

This simple conversational technique effectively puts both people on the same team. "I'm with you! I understand." The counselling skills, including ways to signal empathy, I learned to support my coaching business have been incredibly useful in both my professional and personal lives. The key is not to present your empathetic acknowledgement as a forced, phony statement, like you get these days from many customer service reps reading from a script. A truly genuine, understanding response acknowledging the other person's feelings goes a very long way.

Mind you, you don't have to agree with the opinions, thoughts, and actions of others, but you can always validate their feelings. I recall sharing a tearful moment with my employees during a conversation about issues they'd been having with customer interactions. I didn't necessarily agree with what they'd been doing, but I could totally see that their hearts were in the right place and why they felt misunderstood. With empathy, we build rapport. With apathy, we build walls and barriers. With empathy, we create harmony and, with apathy, we create division. So, I say we usher more empathy into our lives, for everyone's sake.

Now I'd better do some shoulder/arm exercises. Poor me!

Chapter 14
Cancer: The Good, the Bad, and the Ugly

June 13, 2023

ANOTHER BATTLE WON

Linda

We were expecting the post-surgery pathology report to be shared at our meeting with the oncologist last Tuesday, eight days ago. As the day approached – a "deadline" if there ever was one – I observed how detached I felt from the possible verdict. It's as if living with the prospect of death for so long has left me emotionally numb. Taking things one day at a time has been a good coping mechanism if not in fact a credible philosophy, but it also turns the future into a kind of dim, far-off place.

Of course, if I could, I would have chosen to have enjoyed a "complete response" (meaning no cancer cells were found in the tumour that was removed during surgery) over "residual disease" (some cancer cells still remained in the tumour, the surrounding tissue that was also cut out, and possibly elsewhere in my body).

Yet, would the results in the report have changed if I'd wished for a complete response? Logically, our thoughts and desires cannot alter reality. Even so, many people in desperate need of hope continue to imagine that this may be so…and, really, what's the harm?

So, I come to the next meeting assuming 50:50 odds. The younger doctor my oncologist is mentoring has yet to acquire a lot of experience in the field. Presumably, she knows plenty about medicine, but dealing with possibly anxious patients is still new to her. I detect (or maybe project) awkwardness in her first question to us: "Did anyone tell you about the pathology report?" This provides a pretty broad hint about which side of the 50% line I'm about to land on. She is not really asking if I had heard the results from anyone else (because I couldn't have), she simply can't handle being the bearer of this kind of news. Though I'm really the injured party here, my heart can't help going out to her.

One thing I've learnt in my life, sharpening my sensitivity to it during my years of coaching, is that there are ways to soften the impact of bad tidings. Sometimes, our intention is to protect the other party, though more often than not we really want to protect ourselves. The terse, straightforward communication style my breast surgeon uses makes more sense when seen from this perspective: uncomfortable with emotions, she retreats into the facts. How many bad prognoses must she have delivered over the years? It's no surprise that she's developed ways to shield herself from her patients' reactions.

So, the bad news is that I haven't experienced a complete response, as we'd hoped. This means that I'll need to continue with additional chemotherapy instead of just the targeted drug, Herceptin. This prolongs the treatment program to next spring, almost a year away. The disappointment doesn't stop there, though. Apparently, the kind of cancer I have has now been determined to be estrogen-positive.

The results of the first biopsy, all those painful months ago, showed it to be negative. This revelation adds an unexpected five years to my regimen after the current chemo program has been completed.

I am more confused than dismayed by the news. Was there an error in the initial pathology report? Or is my cancer mutating as, somewhat alarmingly, some of them do? Would I have been put on a different treatment program if we'd had this new diagnosis from the beginning? What is my prognosis now? What will be the quality of the life remaining to me? Even with a flurry of questions running through my mind, my solution-orientated, uber-planner side starts weighing the practical implications. We should, for instance, cancel the trip to Korea we scheduled for this fall. I will not be visiting my mother's grave – a major event in Korean culture – any time soon.

Since we've gotten this news, some of my questions have been answered. My prognosis hasn't changed (meaning that I'm more likely to live than die in the near future, barring being run over by a bus or something). The upshot is simply that getting well will be a longer process.

And no, it's highly unlikely that my cancer has mutated. Rather, the first pathology report was probably incomplete; another biopsy at the time almost certainly would've captured the estrogen-positive result. Our oncologist didn't request the second biopsy then because the treatment, either way, would have been identical. I now have a new name for my cancer as my old label "HER2-positive hormone-negative" was found to be incorrect. The "new and improved" term is "triple-positive breast cancer". Which sounds funny and scary in equal measure.

Both as a couple and as individuals, we're pretty resilient and adaptable. We process the new information separately and together, lifting ourselves and each other up along the way. We draw each other's attention to the light. The situation is a long way from perfect, but this doesn't stop us from looking for illumination.

We will play the cards we are dealt. We will focus on what is within our control. We are here today, alive. We cannot even count just how many blessings we enjoy in our lives, including having each other to share this rather bumpy ride with. Some of our friendships have deepened over the last few months and are now beyond price to us. This has been a life-avowing and love-affirming journey, and I don't see it being any different moving forward. Sure, cancer is a terrible affliction. I wouldn't wish it on my worst enemies, including drivers who use their horns for no reason, people who talk in the theatre, and kids who make Tik-Tok videos in public. Yet, a large part of the experience has been extremely sweet. As long as you're willing to embrace and acknowledge the light, you will find that there is plenty to be thankful for.

So, friends, don't be sad for us. Instead, celebrate your and our aliveness with us today, the connections that we nurture, the positive impact that we can still choose to make, and even the unpredictable ups and downs of our lives' trials and triumphs. Because we won't appreciate the highs unless we have been low, just like we won't appreciate life unless death is also part of our reality. We can always find light in the dark, for we can create it from within us.

With acceptance, gratitude, and courage

Yours truly,
Linda

June 16, 2023

IN MY DARKEST HOUR

Håkan

In my darkest hour, I pray
And wonder, could it be?
You are slipping away
Are you slipping away from me?

Your body now battered
but your heart keeps expanding
at peace with all that matters
full of acceptance and understanding

Yeah, life is absurd
But you fill it with so many wonderful things
Joy is always good
And time flies by, as if on wings

But I'm thirsty for more,
Yearning for a bigger share
Not yet ready to let go
Am I too greedy, too unfair?

The greatest adventure of my life
Are you slipping away from me?
Companion, best friend, beautiful wife
You are my true love for all eternity

To listen to the song that resulted from this poem, check out:
https://hawkbjorn.com/in-my-darkest-hour/

Chapter 15
A Longer Road Ahead

July 1, 2023

RESIST OR PERSIST?

Linda

My new chemo drug is called TDM1, or trastuzumab emtansine for short. It is an antibody-drug conjugate, which delivers the cytotoxic agent DM1 specifically to tumour cells with over-expressed HER2 receptors. Yeah, I know. Perfectly clear, right?

As I understand it, TDM1 is a valuable drug for stage-2 cancer because it specifically targets cancerous cells and stops them from creating more. I get this picture of an overly excited school kid volunteering for something, jumping up and down, yelling: "Me, me, me, pick me!!" Except, of course, that children are pretty innocent and cute. HER2 cancer cells aren't.

In theory, this drug is supposed to go after the bad guys only. This is a major improvement compared to my previous chemos, which attacked everything that matched cancer's chemical profile, pretty much indiscriminately. A lot of both healthy and cancerous cells alike were caught up in the battle, leading to a variety of side effects. Although TDM1 is more targeted, it can still spill over into and affect other areas. Like all drugs, this one comes with a warning. In its case, though, this runs to three pages of possible complications.

Today is the day for the first infusion of this new kind of chemo. Håkan and I saunter in thinking this will be over in 30 minutes or so, considering the multiple chemo infusions we've sat through before. We expect this one to consist of only a single IV bag of liquid, not the three or four I've become used to.

So we are surprised, very surprised, not to mention unprepared (no water, no snacks, no earphones for music, no books to read) when the nurse says that it will take up to three hours. The whole time, I am observed with eagle eyes for any toxic or allergic reactions. There is an emergency IV stashed next to my "airline chair", not to mention a whole hospital's worth of emergency equipment in nearby rooms, ready to go if I need to be rescued. I guess the manufacturer wasn't kidding about the possible side effects.

The whole ordeal takes much longer than we'd thought due to all these precautions and the long observation periods. The drug is administered very slowly, drop by drop. Still, in the end, the first session goes uneventfully.

In total, I will be given 14 treatments of this TDM1 stuff, one every three weeks, which adds up to a nine-month-long program. My treatment journey, already protracted, has gotten even longer. It's like the goalposts keep shifting, the milestones I've been expecting to reach getting up and shuffling further off into the distance. I take a deep breath to relax into the new reality. Resisting won't help.

July 21, 2023

(IN) DECISIONS

Håkan

How do we make decisions? With our reason, right, and based on all available information? If we were buying a new car, we would want to know all kinds of facts and figures: the cost, the warranty terms, horsepower and torque, fuel efficiency, available colours, the interior options, etc., etc. And the sales guy would be ready to provide all the details, hard facts, statistics: fixed and irrefutable data. After all that, we'd make our decision based on everything we've learned. (We might still end up buying the car just because it's cool rather than practical, but that's a subject for another book.)

Now, imagine deciding on the pros and cons of radiotherapy after half a year haunted by chemo and surgery. We ask what additional benefits radiation treatment would have. How much would the odds of a full recovery improve? What are the potential side-effects, especially long-term ones that may only show up in 20 years' time? Could suffering through another round of chemo instead be just as effective, especially with the newer, more targeted treatments? What are the stats for survival with and without radiation?

These, and many more, are our questions. And, unlike the hypothetical car sales guy, our doctors are unable to provide hard facts or point to recent, ironclad scientific data. The complexity of cancer is one reason for this ambiguity – it's a hydra rather than a single beast.

Another problem is that reliable research studies take years to complete. By the time the results are out, new chemo treatments are available, new discoveries about specific types of cancer have emerged, and the landscape has changed. Then, added to all this, the enigma is that, even when a stat is available (for example: "90% of women survive this kind of cancer", or "25% experience this severe side effect"), no one can predict which group any given patient might belong to. As a consequence, we and our doctors end up contemplating the probabilities in the vaguest terms. It's like playing a gambling game when you don't know the rules.

So, for the past month, we've been debating, discussing, and deliberating the pros and cons of radiation. Do we still need to go through with this option? After all, the cancer has been removed and the lymph nodes are no longer cancerous. Or is foregoing radiotherapy too much of a risk? Are there cancerous cells, microscopic and invisible to current science, lurking somewhere in Linda's body, just waiting for the chemo poisons to go away?

The answer is a resounding "Maybe!" We don't know for sure, but what we do know is that the monster COULD still be there. Or Linda could be totally cancer-free. There's just no way to check. Following a philosophy of "better safe than sorry," our doctors (all of them) tell us that she should seriously consider five weeks of daily radiation treatments. Just in case, and regardless of the side effects.

And that's where we've finally landed. During a month of meetings, phone calls, poring over research studies online, and long philosophical, existential, exhausting discussions, we weighed whether the risk of long-term harm is worth it based on a possible "maybe". We're going through with it.

My poor darling. I'm sorry in advance for the fatigue you're going to feel. The sleepless nights. The skin burns. The strain on your body and soul. We didn't ask for this. No one ever would.

In the end, it's a leap of faith. It's a question of trusting that we made the best decision based on everything we know and everything we don't know at this moment in time. We shine a light into the darkness and hope, wish and yearn that all will be well in the end. And who can do any better than that?

August 15, 2023

LIFE IS TRANSIENT

Linda

I'm not afraid of death. I'm afraid of a life that's not worth living, though.

I keep coming back to this frightening thought. At one point, the answer seems very clear: absolutely "no" to radiation. The next moment, I am not so sure anymore. What would constitute a life that isn't worth living? What kind of health conditions would put my life in the "more trouble than it's worth" category?

In the end, we decide that radiation and its side effects may be worth the risk, compared to the possibility of cancer recurring and creating havoc all over again. If this happens, it may show up in any part of the body and its vital organs. I haven't made many decisions in life on the basis of "which one is less bad" and having to choose a lesser evil. In a way, one can say that I have been blessed not to be in this situation before.

Still, the decision is behind us. We'll get through it. This, too, will be over soon enough. Radiotherapy is like everything else in life – transient, temporary.

August 21, 2023

WE ARE NOT
WALKING ALONE

Håkan

In the middle of summer, and in the midst of a particularly challenging round of side-effects, sleeplessness, and fatigue, we suddenly feel like getting out into the fresh air and nature. We decide to walk up the steep hill near our home, through Princess Park and then further up onto the Baden Powell Trail. The plan is to walk to Lynn Valley Regional Park and back, around 10 kilometers in total.

It's a beautiful day: perfect temperature, light wind; gorgeous summer weather in British Columbia. Occasionally, we run across a dog walker or a mountain biker but, for the most part, we have the entire forest to ourselves. It feels great to be out, away from the pill bottles, the blankets and pillows, and our other constant reminders of Linda's illness. Sure, the slight headache is still with us, as are the sore scars from the surgery, and the achy muscles too.

But we're walking. Slowly and carefully. Taking in the beauty that surrounds us. Appreciating the tall cedar trees. Listening to the birds chattering around us. And I'm overwhelmed with the feeling that we're part of something so much larger. That we're not walking alone. As we progress along the path, which is blanketed by soft pine and fir needles, a poem forms in my mind:

we are not walking alone

thank god for the wind that's fanning us

thank god for the trees that give us shade
with creatures all around us
and friendships we have made
we are not walking alone

Chapter 16
Out of the Frying Pan

September 3, 2023

BREATHE IN –
BREATHE OUT

Linda

"Breathe in….. a little bit more…now hold….breathe out…"

Just like that, the long-dreaded radiation treatment starts while I'm still suffering a mixed bag of side effects from the new chemo drug or – possibly – aftershocks from the previous treatments. I've been looking forward to the end of radiotherapy before it even began. Anxious as I was, therefore, I wanted to get on with it so I could be done with it.

Here we are, on yet another floor of the hospital that's by now very familiar to both of us. We arrive fortified with hope that's conceivably not misplaced – hope that it will all go well and that I'll have no long-term side effects. Well, there isn't much else we can do apart from hoping. With all the research done and the decision made, we just have to place our trust in the skill and judgment of the professionals.

The stark, cold room furnished with gleaming, high-tech X-ray and radiation machines is more than a little intimidating. Fortunately, the clinical appearance of the equipment makes a conspicuous contrast with the warm and comforting smiles of the ladies in white gowns. It's hard to overestimate how much it means to feel a warm, gentle hand on our shoulders, even for a brief moment, while we feel so vulnerable. In front of this powerful machine, that is exactly how I feel. The humanity of a technician's gentle touch lifts me up a little when I certainly need it.

I also spend a brief moment marvelling at the fact that we submit ourselves to this incredibly harmful force, willingly, in order to be cured. I settle down on the bed under the radiation machine, feeling the full effect of this irony. I also feel the familiar knot in the middle of my chest, where dread resides, tightening.

It seems that precision is everything in radiation treatment. The exact positioning of the body is critical: the radiation beams have to be aimed at precise targets if we are to avoid any unintended consequences, like damage to my lungs or heart. After some fidgeting to ensure that everything is aligned perfectly, the white gowns leave the room to operate the machines from a safe distance. After all, this is bad, bad stuff. The pros who deal with it on a daily basis are only too aware of this fact. They will communicate with me via intercom, I'm told. After taking several X-rays to confirm my positioning once more, everything looks good and we can start the treatment. The breathing prompts start:

"Ok, Linda, when you are ready, take a deep breath in……….. Some more………. Okay, now hold it…………………. (*20 seconds later*)……….. and breathe outtttttt. Well done! Now again, breathe in………. some more, let out a bit and hold……………………………….. Breathe out."

I'm used to controlling my breathing during yoga. Today, the purpose of this is somewhat more critical: if my ribcage is inflated too much or too little, by even a tiny amount, at the moment they zap me, a lot of things can go very wrong.

A few minutes later, I am all done for the day – until the next day. And, although the deep, measured breathing is meant to open up the chest and help deliver the beams to the exact locations, it does something else too — calm my nerves. The contrast between the meditation-like instructions and the deadly ionizing radiation that just passed through my flesh is quite stunning.

Someone in Håkan's circle tells him that 2022 was the worst year of his life. Instantly, my mind turns to the years I've had; some better, some worse, "Then mine was this year – 2023. Or maybe it was 2022, when I was first diagnosed with cancer." Just as quickly, though, I see the futility of this exercise. What could be the point of listing the worst times you've experienced?

Any given moment, day, or year that seems unbearable at the time may turn out to have been a blessing in disguise. Every challenge comes with an associated opportunity: for learning, growing, and possibly unexpected rewards and fulfillment once it's been overcome. Our darkest hours, when we need illumination the most, are often when we realize that embracing our inner light is always possible – not necessarily easy, but unquestionably an option.

So, was 2023 really the worst year of my life so far? On the surface, definitely. And I have to admit that it has been a time of reckoning when it comes to my changing appearance. My identity as a healthy, fit person has been challenged if not, temporarily at least, demolished. My prospects of living a long, healthy, rewarding life have inevitably been called into question.

I experienced many moments and hours of hurt and disappointment, but these also led to finding resilience and strength, and finally brought about a kind of expansion of my inner self. With my physical being diminished, I now search for and cultivate beauty and strength within instead. After all, I do have some control over what goes on inside my heart and head. Dwelling on the aspects of life that are completely out of my hands would bring no rewards.

I pause more these days, taking a moment here and there to catch my breath, center my mind, and take stock. Initially, this was simply because I had very little energy to spare. But I also learnt that fulfillment is not about how much we accomplish, but how much we appreciate what we do. The smallest details carry a heavy weight in teachings, and you can miss a lot if you simply rush past them.

Not being the strongest person in the room, I've learned to accept compassion. By receiving help from others, I've become more familiar with humility – not a quality that played a huge role in my life before.

All my connections with friends and family have evolved into more meaningful ones. In the face of death, we develop into much more authentic people. We are less wasteful with our time. We become brave enough to tell the truth and confess our love.

In fact, this has been a great year, not despite the cancer but because of it. The Yoruba people in West Africa have a saying: "The same rain that falls on the bitter leaves also falls on the sugarcane." Life is full of contradictions. So what if the worst year of my life is also the best?

PRESCRIPTIONS AND POISONS: FINDING THE RIGHT DOSAGE

Håkan

So much, in medicine as in life, comes down to balance. Things that are beneficial when used correctly can become extremely harmful when applied excessively or in the wrong circumstances. Self-confidence, for instance, is typically considered a good characteristic which, however, can easily spill over into arrogance. A strong work ethic is admirable, but not if we allow it to take us away from what's truly important in life and turn it into an obsession with financial success. Even love, when excessive and possessive, can spell all kinds of trouble.

So, how much radiation does a cancer patient need? At what point does it start to do more harm than good? It's a balancing act and finding the right dosage takes careful deliberation, open communication, lots of experience and knowledge which, of course, our health team does its best to provide. Yet, ultimately, it's all about striking a balance, seeing each situation for what it is, and calculating the consequences. As best as we can.

THERE ARE DAYS LIKE THESE

There are days like these
Where nothing's what it seems
There are times like now
We must get through somehow

Everything will still be here tomorrow
What we said today will still be true
Leave the pain, the fears and all your sorrow
Every day that dawns is here anew

There is love like ours
That's bigger than the sea
There's pain like yours
I wish were given me

Everything will still be here tomorrow
What we said today will still be true
Leave the pain, the fears and all your sorrow
Every day that dawns is here anew

There's hope to embrace
And gratitude to make mine
There's life to live
Before we run out of time

To listen to the song that resulted from this poem, check out:
https://hawkbjorn.com/there-are-days-like-these/

Chapter 17
Choices and Contingencies

October 1, 2023

RADIATION BLUR

Linda

I had the last of my daily radiation treatments on September 20th. That means one more milestone passed on this long and challenging journey. However, as we knew would happen, the short-term side effects started in earnest about two weeks after the last treatment. Håkan prepares salt water (1 tablespoon of salt dissolved in a litre of water) every day so we can treat the skin burnt by the imperceptible yet deadly rays.

Several times a day, we have to apply cold compresses that have been soaked in this saltwater solution. Apparently, this helps the skin recover and keeps it from becoming inflamed. In addition, I have a steroid-based lotion to reduce itchiness and Tylenol to help with the sporadic pain in the surgery site. This is a sort of stabbing, needling sensation and is another result of the radiation, which was focused on exactly that spot. A lot has been done to my body in the name of killing cancer or curing me, whichever perspective you come from. No wonder the body complains! So I stir, twitch, flinch, twinge, and shudder due to the discomfort.

Our radiologist predicted that my symptoms would peak about ten days after the last treatment and steadily improve a little bit every day over the next several months. It's remarkable what knowledge does. Just having an idea of what to expect is a sort of comfort against the aches, fatigue, and general irritation. Believing that I'll get better and that this is all temporary makes everything more bearable. A broader perspective on life helps, too.

I wonder how I would have behaved differently in my younger years if I had somehow possessed the life experience I have now. Maybe I would have been more relaxed about a lot of things and, yes, with a lot of people too.

I had a terrible time with my mom's suffering from Alzheimer's in her final years. I wanted nothing more than for her to experience health, comfort, and dignity once more. I hung onto the hope that, although she hadn't had much luck with her origins and circumstances, she could at least spend her life's twilight with self-respect and contentment until the end should come for her. It pained me a great deal to see her gradually losing every aspect of an enjoyable life, including her dignity. I suffered in my heart and body. Maybe I could have handled this struggle with greater grace if I'd had the knowledge I have now.

Attachment to what should be is the source of all suffering, indeed! One of the treasured gifts my illuminating journey over the last several months has given me is the ability to better accept what simply is.

October 26, 2023

EMERGENCY ROOM

Linda

The radiation's side effects are finally starting to subside, as predicted. I'm unclear, however, about where this ever-present fatigue, agonizing headaches, and muscle pains are coming from. Are these still holdovers from the initial chemo treatments, caused by the drug I'm currently on, or a result of the radiation? I wonder, though I have no idea what I'd do with an answer if there were one.

The doctors are now recommending that I start taking hormone modulator pills. This will be – we sincerely hope – the final step in my treatment, though it will last for the next five years. It's not part of the cure *per se*, but it is supposed to help prevent a recurrence of the cancer.

We picked up the first bottle of hormone pills last week from the BC Cancer pharmacy but I've been hesitating, not yet ready to begin taking them. With some of the side effects from the several previous treatments still lingering, I'm hesitant to further assault my already bruised body. Again, a choice I have to make without knowing all the facts!

Do you regret the choices you've made in your life? Or are you one of those who claim: "I don't regret my choices because I don't dwell in the past"? Whenever I hear someone say something like that, I notice hesitation in their voice. Perhaps the more honest response is: "I'm afraid that I'll regret some of what I chose, therefore I don't dare to look back."

How about your choice of career? How would other paths have been different from the one you took instead? Would one route have guaranteed a more fulfilling life than another? In all probability, either path and possibly any of several could have made us happy, albeit with different life experiences along the way.

Someone with a talent for composing and playing music, for instance, may find fulfillment in a PR career. The shape of their life would, of course, be very different from what they would have experienced if they'd become a musician. Maybe a corporate job would have enabled a more comfortable, but less exciting, lifestyle that includes music as a hobby along with other rewarding pastimes like travelling. At the same time, they'd be cut off from certain sources of fulfillment that even struggling musicians can count on, like the joy of creation and fans' applause. Which path would have allowed us to live our vision of an ideal lifestyle more fully, better aligned with who we are? How can anyone, looking backward over the years with the benefit of a broader perspective, gauge which choices they "should" have made?

Back to my decision: I choose not to start hormone therapy just yet, although I will one day soon. Sometimes, delaying the unavoidable is a perfectly respectable third choice.

Then, last night, I ended up in the Emergency Room with a high fever. Since I'm a cancer patient, any fever isn't taken lightly. It can spell all sorts of scary events. They drain blood into fat tubes for culturing, take urine samples, snap X-rays... Lying on the hospital bed under the homogenous white ceiling and harsh fluorescent lights, I mutter to myself: "Thank God I didn't pile on the hormone modulator!" We would've assumed that it was the new medicine that was causing havoc, wasting time and potentially skewing the diagnosis.

As it turns out, I am sent home at an ungodly hour with most of the scarier possibilities ruled out except for one: a blood infection. Blood culture tests will take two days to supply an answer. My temperature has gone up and down in dramatic arcs ever since. I learn (or maybe re-learn) one thing about myself: I'm really not very good at being sick.

Returning to the topic of choices: what decision can you make today to create a more fulfilling life? What other choices will you need to make to create the results you desire? There's always uncertainty about where you will end up, but one thing is for sure: if you don't choose, another force will choose for you.

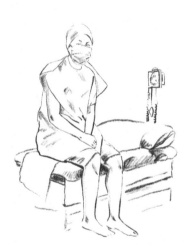

Chapter 18
Life Goes On

November 6, 2023

LIVELY OR LIFELESS?

Linda

One of the professionals I hired a couple of weeks ago for my book project wonders out loud what my energy level must be like when I'm at my usual 100% if what he was seeing was my compromised 60-80%. It's meant to be a compliment (I think!)

* Yes, I wrote and published a business coaching book during my cancer treatment journey called "Scale Your Small Business: The Definitive Guide to a Sustainable Business and Fulfilling Life". You can find it on any of your favourite book stores.

This reminded me of the consistent reaction when meeting friends over the past year, who often commented on how "normal" I appeared (minus my hair, of course). They anticipated seeing a scrawny, pale and lifeless version of myself battling cancer. I don't blame them because I expected the same – a beat-up tired and worn shell – for a while, anyhow.

To my surprise and that of my friends, we cancer patients have a lot more life in us than many may expect – though, of course, I'm speaking in relative terms here. True, we are not in our best shape, and this is reflected in how we look and act. Even so, our compromised selves have their own ambitions and passions. Some of these were showcased at a workshop that I went to organized by Look Good, Feel Better (LGFB) a couple of months ago.

These workshops are ongoing events and teach cancer patients about how to wear makeup safely when our bodies are extra sensitive to the sun, germs and viruses (and many other unnamed things you'd normally not give a second thought) and how to wear wigs and other head coverings. Some attendees hadn't lost their hair yet, some had lost every last strand (including me), and some hadn't even started any chemo but were anticipating – and dreading – the inevitable side effects. I was curious about how other women choose to walk journeys parallel to mine and how they face all the challenges in their own individual ways. There is comfort in numbers and knowing you're not the only one contending with these difficulties.

We all looked different: some flaunted their hairless heads (stark-looking even to me), some wore beanies and toques, and some others walked around with full heads of hair (their own or a borrowed coiffure). Some intended to try their best to protect their pre-cancer image, most aspired only to hang on to a part of their former looks, and others fully accepted the new norm. Regardless, everyone was dealing with it, boldly, on their own terms.

A lot of people mentioned that I was brave in the way I faced my cancer treatments. I'm still trying to understand what that means. "Bravery" would imply that I had a choice, that I could have chosen not to face cancer, but I didn't, did I? To survive and live, ideally in good health, is above everything an instinct, not a desire or ambivalent preference. I don't know if acting according to our innate biological programming constitutes bravery.

So, bravely or not, at different stages of our cancer journey, we react and respond to the disease and its treatments in our own ways. I decided to walk my journey more publicly than I would have chosen normally, even publishing a blog and now a book. What prompted me to choose this direction? Processing and sharing my journey openly offered a chance to demystify the disease, especially in terms of how *I* chose to deal with it. It also allowed me to show that I appreciated the empathy and support that poured in from all sides.

Even now, I don't understand my motivation fully. I do, however, feel that choosing to share my experiences has been a blessing and has made me feel more connected with the universe. We are not alone in this world. Division, hate and extremism only rear their heads when we're isolated and base our thinking on separation. Unity, love and harmony should be our natural inclination; the openness we all crave arises when we interact, listen and share.

Eleven months into my cancer treatments, Håkan and I assess my energy levels and decide that we'll take a trip to Arizona – one we were meaning go on when life had other plans – in between chemo sessions. These are three weeks apart, so we'll have a good few days to relax and indulge our love of nature (not to mention escaping the dreary weather of Vancouver in the late fall).

One idea that used to be theoretical for me but is now a concrete reality is that life cannot be taken for granted. So, we'll take the plunge, and we will deal with any medical challenges *if* they show up while we're on the road. We pack a few zillions of pill bottles, some of which I take regularly and others we'll need in case of various side effects. I wonder what the notorious TSA will make of my ambulant pharmacy.

We probably cannot manage a full-day, 32-kilometer round-trip hike to the bottom of the Grand Canyon and we probably cannot do some other things we'd otherwise enjoy either. But that's okay. I embraced the value of "acceptance" at the beginning of my cancer journey and so I shall continue. For I am grateful that we can enjoy nature. It, too, is part of the bigger universe that we need to integrate into our larger selves.

November 15, 2023

5 YEARS TO LIVE

Linda

No, that's not my prognosis but a deliberate point of reflection. For the most part, I feel that I've been dealing with cancer's challenges with some fortitude, taking things one day at a time. Then, as life often does, it staggers my confidence: this time, it's Håkan's turn to experience a health scare. Very quickly, my supposed courage collapses into a deep well of sorrow that I haven't felt in a while.

That's when the poem "Two in a Boat" spins back into my consciousness. I realized that I was taking too much credit for enduring the various discomforts of my journey, when in fact it was my partner who fortified me and nourished me all the while.

Two in a boat

There are two of them
In a boat,
One reads the stars,
The other finds the way through the storms,
When one navigates the stars,
The other leads through the storms,
And then, at the end, at the very end,
They'll remember
The sea was blue.

$\qquad$ —Reiner Kunze *(Translation by Victoria Ichizli-Bartels)*

After the scare, we sit together and talk. We are all born into this world and, from that day on, we walk toward death. Without exception, we will all die. With very few exceptions, we don't know exactly when our time on earth will expire. With that sobering, yet illuminating reality brought into the forefront of our minds – again – we decide to live the next five years as if they are going to be our last. And this is not too far-fetched of a possibility for us.

A life unlived and unexplored wouldn't count for much, even if we had 50 years left together. If we can instead live right now, fully present and appreciating the beauty of all things in the world, even 5 days in each other's company would be better.

So, you may ask: "Why five years? Why not just one month? It would make life seem even more precious, wouldn't it?" It's just that I find it harder to think within such a short timeframe and make meaningful, realistic plans – living in the moment doesn't have to mean abandoning all forethought. In our case, the first thing we tackle is updating our top destinations to explore worldwide. If we only have five years, we reason, we better prioritize!

As it stands, I still have to visit a Vancouver hospital for tri-weekly chemo treatments, so going far away will be tricky for the time being. We settle on Arizona. We had planned to go last winter to see the deserts but my cancer diagnosis rudely interfered. Arizona is relatively close by. If something bad should happen, direct flights offer easy access to our medical system if needed. So, Arizona it is.

Aside from exploring the world, what other desires does expecting a shorter lifespan highlight? Will we see more of our family? Will we visit certain friends more often? Will it be different with them now that there's a sense of finality to our relationships? Probably, right?

Håkan says he wants to write enough songs for one more album. Perhaps I write a book with my mom as a subject. Will these creations add anything to this world? My hope is that they will. With so much turmoil and darkness around us, spreading a little light can only be a good thing. So we will. Continue to breathe. Continue to appreciate the beauty of living. Be generous. Be kind. As I write these words, the sun is just emerging outside our Arizona window. I will open the blinds fully and let the light in.

November 16, 2023

HOME

Håkan

When I left my comfort zone, my home, my parents, all of my friends, my language and my culture all behind at the age of 17 as an exchange student to the US, I think I realized for the first time in life how alone we really are. Yes, we have friends and surround ourselves with familiar things and routines as best as we can, to help fight off this ur-loneliness. But it's always present, in one way or another.

During the life I've shared with Linda and the years we've spent charting a joint course, everything "us" has given me the elusive home I think we all yearn for. And it's a mutual experience. We both live in a country that we weren't born in. We both speak a language other than our native tongue. Neither one of us is tied to a place, a hometown, or childhood room and a past in which our friends and family still live on. We are floating in this world like dandelion seeds in the wind. But we stick together. And we have each other. We gave each other home.

November 17, 2023

CANCER OR NOT, ARIZONA

Linda

Cancer or not, Arizona
Here we come
Finally, Arizona
One full year later
You waited for us
And welcomed us
Warm and dry,
Just the way we like it
Nature all around
So ancient, so primordial that
Wisdom practically oozes out of you!

Tylenol as my new best friend,
Lots of rest in between,
We explore Antelope Valley,
Jaw-dropping Grand Canyon,
Redder than red red rocks of Sedona.

Sonora Desert, so arid
So much sun
And so little water
Maybe a lesson for not going to the extreme in life, or
Maybe, why not?

The desert teaches resilience
Resilience of life

Life has its own momentum.
So ride with it,
Live for it,
Thrive in it.

You may wonder: "Couldn't we have waited to travel until the treatments were completed? What if you get sick on the road? What if you have to cancel the trip halfway through?" Reasonable questions, sure. Here is the thing: what is ever guaranteed in our lives? How do we know with certainty that next year will come for us? We simply can't take it for granted. My fitness level is compromised, and we won't go on as many nor as strenuous hikes as we would have otherwise. That's okay. What matters is that we live now, as best we can. We can't wait for tomorrow to start seeking fulfillment. So here we are, travelling, marvelling at the gorgeous views, expansive spaces and life, well, life really is beautiful!

Chapter 19
Eyes on the Horizon

December 13, 2023

(on my document birthday: that is a separate story altogether)

SEASON FINALE

Linda

This is the last month in the year-long journey Håkan and I have walked with cancer. I've endured the whole enchilada: the hard chemos, the surgeries, the radiation, and, now, the second round of chemo. I also finally started my hormone inhibitors, minimizing the chance of any cancer recurring and consequently maximizing my chance of living a long life.

So, what's the chance of this happening? I can count on a five-year survival rate in the mid-80th percentile or, conversely, a non-survival rate of about 15%. On the surface, it looks good. The odds are in my favour. The reality is this: one in eight women in North America will be diagnosed with breast cancer. 87.5% won't get it, 12.5% will. These are the facts. I drew the short straw and belong to the latter group. Though I could have had a complete response after the first round of chemo (over 65% of patients in my position do), I didn't and again I belong to the minority.

I'm not really a pessimist and I don't consider myself particularly unlucky. It's just that, when it comes to cancer, I've learned to accept complete surprises. I don't take life for granted anymore. That is the first and most important lesson I learned during the past year.

Will I be alive in five years or not? I don't know but, realistically, neither does anyone else. Do I need to be reassured that I will survive cancer? My answer may surprise you: "No, I don't." It's not because I don't value my life. On the contrary, I like living very much.

My second lesson learned is this: it's not how long we live but how well we live. However short or long our time on earth might be, fulfillment comes not from duration but significance. I have been given more life during this year than any other. Because I was made conscious of it. With the lived wisdom of a fleeting life, I appreciated the world and the people and all things in it that much more.

Håkan just joined me at my table and I asked him what he learned himself:

Håkan

That life is so precious. And that nothing can ever be taken for granted. This is a hard lesson because we really, really want our lives to be rooted in certainty and stability. So it's hard to acknowledge that we can't ever count on knowing what will happen next. We try to figure out what's coming. And we say that we're going to visit our families in Korea and Sweden next year, 2024. We plan it, book it, announce it. But we can't know that we will actually get there.

This all sounds a little exasperating. But strangely, this past year I've also become aware of a serenity that I didn't know before. A kind of peace and calm in the face of uncertainty. An urge to slow down, have another look, say another kind word, let my gaze rest just a little longer, not rush off to do the next thing. It's a tranquil place to be. And a gift.

So is the subtle melancholy that invisibly creeps into the most unexpected moments and situations. It's a sweet kind of sadness, full of gratitude. Just today, Linda and I are sitting on our glassed-in patio, illuminated by the sun which is unshrouded by clouds, a rare event in December's Vancouver. We're surrounded by gently swaying evergreens and vibrant leafy laurels, squirrels hopping between the plants, hopelessly searching for wherever they buried their food in August. I'm sipping freshly brewed coffee and Linda hot green tea. This is the life! Here, present together. Cozy and grateful. It could end right now and this would have been the best moment of my life.

Yeah, I think so.

Linda

Yes, life is exactly as it should be. That includes cancer. We have received such care, kindness and generosity from friends and strangers alike, from the moment we found out right up to the present day. Having received, we also learn to give. We are more generous and kinder to people now, including ourselves. That, too, is a great lesson.

We dwell less on things that are not going to add to our quality of life because time is precious. The value of our time has appreciated significantly. We are more judicious in how we spend it and that is also a valuable lesson. We may all live 90 years but, if we were to sleepwalk through it, what would be the point? Instead, we can now value the most precious resource we have – time – as we should and live true to ourselves.

With a few months of chemotherapy still remaining, and some side effects of various treatments still stubbornly hanging on, we soldier on with acceptance, gratitude and courage.

Signing off With Abundance of
Love and Light

Linda & Håkan

ACKNOWLEDGMENTS

We are greatly indebted to our editor extraordinaire, Victor Prozesky, for his brilliance in editing guidance, encouragement and professionalism.

And you, dear reader. Thank you for purchasing our book and sharing our story. Our journey continues, of course, into the new year and hopefully many years to come. We plan to do everything we can to remain healthy and continue to live sustainable and fulfilling lives, for ourselves and for our community. This means we're continuing our sustainable lifestyle and practicing kindness to all beings. Be kind to our planet, each other and yourself. And most of all, be well!

Love and Light!
Linda and Håkan

Made in the USA
Monee, IL
16 June 2024

59987030R00100